Breaking Free from Depression

David Hazard

HARVEST HOUSE PUBLISHERS
Eugene, Oregon 97402

Cover by Left Coast Design, Portland, Oregon

Advisory

Readers are advised to consult with their physician or other medical practitioner before implementing the suggestions that follow.

This book is not intended to take the place of sound medical advice or to treat specific maladies. Neither the author nor the publisher assumes any liability for possible adverse consequences as a result of the information contained herein.

BREAKING FREE FROM DEPRESSION
Copyright © 2002 by David Hazard
Published by Harvest House Publishers
Eugene, Oregon 97402

Library of Congress Cataloging-in-Publication Data
Hazard, David.
    Breaking free from depression / David Hazard.
      p. cm.—(Healthy body, healthy soul series)
    Includes bibliographical references
    ISBN 0-7369-0482-4
    1. Depression, Mental—Popular works. 2. Self-help techniques. I. Title.

RC537 .H385 2001
616.85'27—dc21   2001024464

Printed in the United States of America.

03 04 05 06 07 / BP-MS / 10 9 8 7 6 5 4

Contents

Books by David Hazard
in the Healthy Body,
Healthy Soul Series

Reducing Stress
Breaking Free from Depression
Building Cancer Resistance

Future Releases
Relieving Headaches and Migraines
Controlling PMS
Managing Your Allergies

Healthy Body, Healthy Soul

From across the ages comes the psalmist's vision of mankind: We are "fearfully and wonderfully made." Body and soul are intricately woven together, made to balance and support each other. And when our lives are in balance we experience an overall kind of wellness…a sense of buoyancy and wholeness.

But when something is out of balance, the wonder and awesomeness of being alive slowly erode. We can find ourselves slipping into a gray mood…then into a long "flat" stretch in which not much appeals to us any more…then into lethargy…until eventually we find ourselves stuck in depression.

Breaking Free from Depression, like each book in the Healthy Body, Healthy Soul series, offers simple and practical strategies you can easily adapt to your need, lifestyle, and preference.

Like the other books in this series, this volume is not offered as a substitute for support you may need from a healthcare professional such as a doctor, psychiatrist, psychological counselor, or from a member of the clergy who's qualified to counsel.

All depression should be taken seriously. Some forms cannot be treated without the care of professionals. And even "mild" recurring or ongoing depression should be a signal that you need to seek qualified help.

Nonetheless, we are ultimately responsible for our own self-care, and we can do a great deal to help ourselves break free from depression. For that reason, this book takes a "whole-person" approach to restoring inner wellness again. From that perspective, it offers a wide range of strategies that can complement your work with a healthcare professional.

With that in mind, this book can help you…

- *assess* various aspects of your life and determine which are contributing to your depressive state

- *create a personal plan*, with simple things you can do to reverse depression

In these pages, you'll find many simple remedies that can turn your life around and make it—believe it or not—better than ever before. To help you build the whole-life plan that works best for you, you'll be given…

- *easy "mind-lifting" techniques you can use anytime, anywhere*
- *ways to boost your spirit*
- *information on foods that are wonderfully "mood lifting"*
- *creative strategies for changing "downer" relationships*
- *fitness discoveries that will get you up out of your seat—and moving again!*
- *guidance about healing herbs and supplements*

…and much more practical information.

Throughout, you will also encounter informational sidebars and quotes to lift your soul. All in all, these great ideas will help to lift your whole life…and bring you health, body and soul.

David Hazard
Founder of The New Nature Institute

① Need a Lift?

*I*f you're reading this book—*congratulations.* You're among the relatively small handful of people who are willing to take an active role in dealing with their depression.

Wait a minute, you're thinking. *How can that be true?* You may have in mind all the recent news stories about the millions of men, women, and even children now taking prescription drugs to treat their depression. Most of us know someone who is taking Celexa, Paxil, Prozac, Wellbutrin, Zoloft, or another antidepressant drug. Not only that, the media have been full of stories about the huge wave of people trying to combat depression with natural mood-lifting substances like St. John's Wort.

If you're dealing with depression—yours or someone else's—a pharmaceutical drug or a natural supplement may well be an important part of your strategy. They can give you that quick sense of inner "buoyancy" and keep you from sinking.

But as any health professional will tell you, depression is a condition that has a wide-ranging impact in our lives. It can "spread" throughout our whole being, until body, mind, and spirit are all involved. Unfortunately, as a culture (and by human nature) we'd love to just pop something in our mouth and be "cured." But taking a pill will never resolve the other life factors that are weighing down on us.

For these reasons, the best strategy for dealing with depression is one that takes a *whole-person* approach, as this book does. When body, mind, and spirit are working together, we experience the wholeness, well-being, and quality of life we're looking for.

The Creeping Shadow

One of the characteristics of many depressed people is that they often don't see how depression is spreading throughout their whole life.

Depression is like a shadow cast by the sun as it sinks. The shadow creeps along, growing longer...engulfing more of the land...until, suddenly—darkness prevails.

Our tendency is to think we can "confine" depression to one part of our life. We may say, "I know I'm a little down...but it's not affecting my work." (Though it is.) Or "I've been depressed—but I'm handling it so well at home I doubt my spouse and kids know something's wrong." (They do.) We don't see how depression is gaining ground, but it is.

Sometimes depression is triggered by an event or a disorder in one aspect of our life...and we don't make the connection between the trigger and the depression for some time. Once again, it spreads from one part of our life to another and "creeps up" on us.

Consider these three scenarios:

Thomas

Over a period of weeks Thomas lost his appetite. Then he began to feel mildly nauseated much of the time. He also could not shake off exhaustion, and when he was not at work he slept all the time. This hadn't been the case six months earlier...that is, before he and his long-time girlfriend broke up.

During a checkup at the doctor's, he mentioned his distress over losing Cherise. In fact there were many losses he'd never talked to anyone about "because I didn't think they mattered that much—I thought I was over all that stuff." This was the doctor's clue, of course. After looking at Thomas's whole health picture, they concluded together that his emotional letdown was triggering a physiological response, resulting in loss of appetite, mild stomach distress, and the deepening exhaustion.

Thomas was going to have to learn a new strategy for handling emotional losses. Ignoring them had only built a dismal interior atmosphere into which a depressive low was able to settle like a dark fog. And it had triggered physical problems as well.

Karin

Karin was a really "up" person. Growing up, she'd been a topflight student and athlete. Now, in her real estate career she was a top seller. Then, over a six-month period she suddenly dropped a lot of weight. She felt anxious…then depressed. Then came big mood swings, but after each small "up" came a deeper, longer "down."

It's all the pressure at work, she told herself. *The competition is getting to me. After this season I'll take a vacation. Then I'll slow things down, and maybe get into the church work I used to enjoy. If I start making a meaningful contribution with my life again, that's got to help.*

But before she could make those changes, the depression and other symptoms got worse. When Karin mentioned the problem to her minister, she thought he'd offer something inspiring to read and suggest she take a shift at the church's soup kitchen. (When she was growing up, her pastor was big on saying, "When you do for other people, you don't have time to sit around and feel bad about yourself.") Instead, following his instincts, this man sent her for a blood test.

The test confirmed his suspicion: adult-onset diabetes. In Karin's case, a physiological problem was the big underlying cause of her depression and the dramatic weight loss.

Medication and the right diet changed Karin's health picture. As it turned out, she also decided to "correct" her intense work-focus by slowing down her life. Helping at the soup kitchen was another important change she decided to make in the interest of lifting her spirit. As Karin began to find the whole-life strategy that worked for her, she came out of depression.

Mike

"Vice President of Marketing." That's what the sign on the door of Mike's new office read. But it seemed like the higher he climbed on the success ladder, the more cynical he became. His second wife was always unhappy, and now she was talking about leaving. Most discussions with his son deteriorated into heated arguments…then cold silence. They had a very comfortable life—so what if he wasn't around a lot and they didn't have a close family. Who did?

Mike began telling himself, *Life just stinks.*

On better days, he told himself that the financial success and all the "toys" it bought him were some compensation, at least. But then even his two great loves, sailing his yacht and collecting antique pistols, began to no longer make him happy.

One morning Mike looked at himself in the mirror. He was overweight and probably at risk of a heart attack. He had few good friends, unless you counted a couple of golf buddies who regularly put up with his complaints for 18 holes. He'd been "down" for so long he could hardly remember what "up" was like.

That was the moment Mike admitted, *My life has no meaning. ...And though I supply my family with lots of expensive stuff, I've given them very little in the way of beliefs and values. Just my cynicism. If my life has some great purpose, I have no clue what it is.*

Mike discovered, of course, that one cause of serious depression is spiritual emptiness. As is true with all depression, its damaging effects spread to his attitudes about work and relationships, and even undermined his ability to experience a lift from simple recreation.

Fortunately, Mike realized he was in deep trouble when suicidal thoughts kept playing at the edges of his mind. He then reached out for both medical and spiritual help, and the combination of good spiritual direction and physical care lifted him out of depression.

BEFORE YOU READ FURTHER

~

If you are severely depressed—suffering from distressful thoughts of harming yourself or others...or experiencing bouts of confusion...or not eating...or if you are unable to function at home or at work...*put down this book and call a healthcare professional now.* (If you don't know a counselor or therapist, your family physician, local hospital, or the mental health department in your city or county can help you locate one.)

Physiological ailments and disorders can also be triggered by depression of even mild intensity, especially if the depression is chronic. If you've been "down" for weeks or months *and* you're experiencing physical distress of some kind, *call a healthcare professional today for an appointment.*

You may in fact be a strong person. But if you're seriously or chronically depressed, you've already been carrying too great a weight for too long. Place your need in the caring hands of someone who can help.

Beware the Tricky Nature of Depression

These three case stories tell us a few important things about the nature of depression.

The Cause(s) of Depression Can Hide

If we've been generally healthy, like Karin for example, we may completely overlook a physical problem that's making us run down and that's triggering depression.

Keep in mind that depression can become *hidden* if we have a natural tendency to minimize our problems and symptoms. This is often the case with very capable people. We mask our problems with a facade of "can-do" determination. We get by in life telling ourselves, *What I'm feeling is no big deal. I can handle this.* For some of us that's a fact. We *can* handle a lot. But when we think this way, we condition ourselves to accommodate way too many dark and dismal moods—until feeling down seems pretty normal. By then we've lost sight of the truth that we're depressed!

The question that very capable, "can-do" people should ask is not, *Can I handle this depression?* The question is this: *Why should I make myself live with depression any longer?*

Even if we get beyond this problem of mental conditioning, as these case stories show, there are other reasons the source of our depression can hide. A physical illness may "fly below the radar" of medical testing for some time before emerging in recognizable symptoms. An emotional trigger—say, a difficult event we thought we'd handled well at the time—may have left long-lasting shock waves in our spirit. For this reason alone we need to take a whole-person approach as we look for ways to treat our depression.

Untreated Depression Will Engulf More of Our Life

Since our body, mind, and spirit are so closely connected, it's only a matter of time until the whole of our life is affected by a single source of depression. The problem may begin as, say, a physical illness that causes pain or loss of energy. Given enough time—or if it's a severe enough problem—it will always affect our mental attitude and our spiritual outlook.

Because depression spreads inside us and carries our whole being down, it pulls us into a state of being that can best be thought of as a downward spiral. Like a plane that loses control, depression picks up a negative energy of its own until our whole world seems to be on a crash course.

To get a feel for how this depressive spiral works, we might picture it like this:

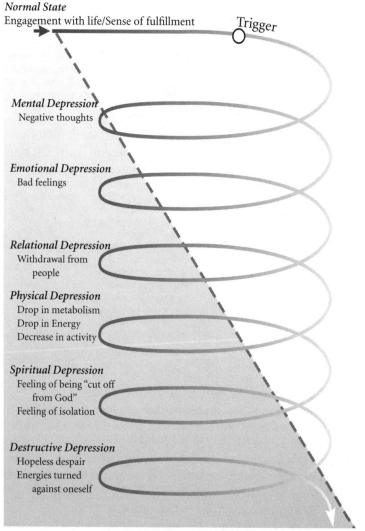

Normal State
Engagement with life/Sense of fulfillment   Trigger

Mental Depression
Negative thoughts

Emotional Depression
Bad feelings

Relational Depression
Withdrawal from
people

Physical Depression
Drop in metabolism
Drop in Energy
Decrease in activity

Spiritual Depression
Feeling of being "cut off
from God"
Feeling of isolation

Destructive Depression
Hopeless despair
Energies turned
against oneself

Lowest State
Disengagement from life/Sense of total emptiness

Look at the illustration on the previous page and consider the depressive spiral that a guy named Andy often experiences.

Something triggers a "down" mood, and immediately Andy's emotional outlook suffers. Though he may not voice it, his attitude about his relationship to other people gets pulled into the downward spiral. He feels upset, or angry, or just disconnected.

At this point, Andy can tell himself a number of things, like: *No one needs to hear another person's complaints. It wouldn't be fair to dump my problems on someone else.* Or: *I can handle this on my own.* Or: *Nobody really cares anyway, so I might just as well keep my problems to myself.*

The weight of these emotions makes Andy feel physically restless and agitated at first. Upset and anger are uncomfortable emotions, so he tries to shrug them off. But pretty soon he loses the motivation to do much of anything. He feels sluggish. In time, he finds himself waking up from a full night's sleep with a bonedeep weariness that makes him wish he didn't have to roll out of the sack, much less face another day. As his metabolism turns down, his digestion slows and his body chemistry functions at less than optimum.

What started as a single event is spreading out and engulfing more territory. Andy now finds it hard to concentrate during important meetings at work. He has trouble calling up details from his memory. Reasoning his way to solutions feels like way too much work, so even simple problems start to appear overwhelming. He begins to fear he's going to fail at his job...but he can't think of what he'll do if he tanks and gets fired.

As he spirals down, Andy feels like a deer freezing in the headlights. Even simple tasks and decisions are hard. That's because he's sensing that life is slipping out of his control. Decisions and demands are piling up, and he's feeling less and less capable of making good choices. It's like he's bracing for a crash.

The depressive spiral deepens and affects his view of life. He thinks, *Maybe life itself is just lousy. Maybe there's nothing and no one "out there"—not even God—to give me any reason to hope things can be better.* Now the depression has embedded itself in Andy's spirit.

Unfortunately, the other areas of Andy's life have been on the slide all this time too. Sadly, he may be blind to this overall downturn. Andy, like most of us, will tend to focus on the fact that he is "doing okay" in some other aspect of his life, in this case his work. But now that depression is taking hold, that's more illusion than reality. When we're depressed, every part of our life is brought down in some way, whether or not we recognize it. (More about this in a minute.)

Even if we consider our depression to be "mild," it *will* tip us into this downward and accelerating spiral. That's the nature of depression.

Depression Destroys

Remember Mike, our cynical vice president? He had a lifelong habit of valuing material things over emotional connections and spiritual values. Without knowing it, his depressive thinking gradually colored all his relationships. ("People always have their hand out. They always want something." Translated: "They don't really care about *me*. They care about what I can do and what I can give them.") We can easily see how this outlook withered his ability to form mutually supportive bonds, even with his family.

The destructive path of depression didn't stop with the deterioration of Mike's relationships, sad to say. Eventually it destroyed his ability to put energy into his work. Finally, it sapped his ability to derive pleasure and esteem from career accomplishments on one hand, or from recreation on the other. If he hadn't responded to a "wake-up call" inside, it might even have led him to commit an ultimate act of destruction.

Depression causes our lives to deteriorate in other ways, too.

Physiologically, it slows the metabolism. It lowers our immune response and weakens our resistance to disease. It leaves the digestive system sluggish and affects the absorption of nutrients. It slows respiration, lowers the blood's oxygen level, and leaves toxins and damaging free-radicals to circulate in the blood longer.

Spiritually, depression cuts us off from the awareness of sacred realities. We lose the sense that God is present with us and at work in every aspect of our lives. We lose our ability to recognize the common graces that come to us as gifts through other people, through nature, and through those miraculous, wonderful "coincidences" that happen along the way.

Mentally, depression plays havoc with our brain chemistry. We are impaired in our ability to call on all areas of the brain, which we need for healthy reasoning, imagining, creating, and decision-making.

Sometimes We Need to Rely on Other People's Assessments

There is one more thing we need to know about the nature of depression: *Depression tends to blind us to the truth about our ability to manage life.* A moment ago we saw how a guy named Andy clung to the fact that he was "doing okay" at work. That was his barrier of defense against the greater truth that depression was slowly engulfing his whole life.

Here it is, folks: Inner barriers protect us from focusing on unpleasant truths. Unfortunately, many of us spend a lot of energy defending against truths we need to face.

Yes, it's normal to want to see ourselves as healthy, functioning adults. We like it when we can handle life, manage our stuff, keep it all together. Then we feel capable, self-sufficient, independent. *Adult.* The dark side of this is that we hate to see ourselves as needing help. Admitting that something has overwhelmed our defenses is like admitting we're not capable adults.

Natural defensiveness makes it hard to be honest with ourselves when depression is getting the better of us. This same defensiveness will also make it hard to truly listen when someone else says, "You seem depressed." We naturally resort to our "I'm okay—really" line of protection.

Let's say they persist: "Then why are you acting depressed?" They give a list of observations.

This is the point at which they may get a bullet in response from us, like "I'm *fine*" or "I can handle it"—or even "Get off my back."

The nature of depression—and our good old human nature—will tend to blind us to the truth about our condition. For this very reason, we *need* other people *around* us to tell us what they see going on *in* us.

Don't Shoot!

Think of it this way. Depression is like a dark funnel cloud forming at your back. Pretty soon this destructive tornado will start pulling in more and more of what lies in its path. Sometimes you can tell it's headed your way. But sometimes you need someone watching your back for you. Someone to say, "Look out! Something bad is headed your way." So, if someone in your life is asking, "Why are you depressed?"—put down your weapons.

We all need to pay attention when someone expresses concern. We need to open up, be honest, and talk. Maybe part of our problem is that we've never learned to build good bonds of openness, honesty, and trust to begin with. Maybe facing the truth—that right now we're depressed and needing support—will give us a great reason to start.

Give Depression the Boot

Many of us who have lived with depression just don't believe life can be any different. That's a fact. We've probably been too accommodating and made way too much room in our lives for this unwelcome stranger. Too many of us settle for a life that's less than whole. That's also a fact.

Let's set out from the get-go with a firm grip on this *new* fact: *We can open a new door and leave depression to fend for itself.* We can choose a life of wholeness.

This book can help you open that new door to wholeness. Opening it will lead you to new and transforming attitudes about yourself and others and life. This small volume will give you solid, helpful information that will carry you from where you are now to where you want to be—living your life, directing your life, on top of your life...instead of feeling you're on the bottom of it.

Today, why not choose the path to wholeness and start to reverse depression's downward spiral? Guaranteed—you'll find yourself beginning the refreshing walk that leads you up and out...into a *whole* new life.

(2)

"Mapping" Your Depression

*E*ven for those of us who suffer lifelong from bouts of depression, there are usually times when we're *up.*

Have we ever stopped to ask ourselves, "What is it that
sends me *down* into the depression spiral?" Or "Once I'm in it, how
does it spread and take over my life?"

We can learn to recognize the things that trigger depression. We
don't need to find ourselves on a dead-end street, feeling powerless,
feeling like there is no way out. And we can use our knowledge to
help create a "map" that can lead us back up and out of depression.

We Think We Know...But Do We Really?

"I already know what makes me depressed," says Ray. "It's a visit
from my parents. They're so critical...." Then he pauses. "Well, I
guess I also get depressed when a project at work gets stalled. But
that's just because I get frustrated...."

Keri, his wife, disagrees. "Ray *used* to get depressed only once in
awhile. Now he's down most of the time. I don't think he even
knows when and why it first began. But almost any little thing can
trigger an emotional slump now."

Ray nods sheepishly. "Yeah. I guess she's right. I used to think I
knew what made me feel down. But after being this down, this long,
I really don't know anymore. *Lots* of things trigger it now."

For each of us, depression usually has many different triggers.
Whether we're working with a professional or dealing with depression on our own, we'll make greater strides toward wellness, if we
take time to study our darker moods and understand ourselves.

17

For most people, depression usually doesn't originate from just one source, but from several. Do you and I even know what might trigger our depression? With this important self-knowledge we can start to equip ourselves to avoid depressive slumps.

As we go through this process, we gain perspective on our lives, which is vastly important. We begin to see the overall "map." We start to notice when, where, why, and how down moods begin. We become able to anticipate situations and conditions that are likely to trigger depression and can then plan courses of action that can lead us more quickly out of depressive moods when they strike.

You, and You Alone

Creating a personal map to help you deal with depression can be one of the most significant steps you take in redrawing the course of your life from today forward. With a little bit of patience and work, you'll be making a heroic effort on behalf of your total well-being.

I want to emphasize that this is work that only you can do. No doctor, counselor, therapist, spouse, or loving friend can do this *for* you. And no one can do it *better* than you can. I am making a point of how important mapping your depression is for one important reason: When we're in a depressive slump we don't feel like expending *any* effort. We'd rather rely on someone else—a professional, or a caring companion—to expend the energy for us. "Just tell me what to do, and I'll do it. Just don't ask me to do anything more than that right now."

Sometimes severe and chronic depressions require outside intervention, that's true. But after any intervention, achieving long-term freedom from depression requires *our* effort. Living free from depression requires a devotion on our part—a commitment to changing our own selves. Until we take ownership of caring for ourselves, we can only expect limited and temporary results.

Getting free of depression requires life changes that no one else can make for us. Are you willing to make a commitment to your self and your future? Consider this before you commit to this lifelong effort.

Three Gifts You Need

Learning to care for your self may be the most important life change you will ever make. That requires us to give ourselves three gifts:

Time • Attention • Care

This may not be as easy as it sounds. Some of us aren't very good at taking care of our selves and our needs. We *minimize* our needs, and tell ourselves things like, *Just get over it. Get on with life.*

Or we *"should"* ourselves to death. We *should* be thinking of others. We *should* be serving our family, our community. We *should* be increasing our net worth, or helping humanity, or serving God. When it comes to a commitment to our selves and our important personal needs…gosh, that sounds too selfish.

Maybe we even *berate* and *accuse* ourselves with thoughts like, *What a weakling you are. No wonder you've wound up in depression.* Maybe we compare ourselves too much. *My grandmother survived the Great Depression by working four back-breaking jobs, while raising three kids on her own—and she was never depressed.*

Has self-neglect, self-abuse, or negative comparison *ever* helped *anyone*? Right now, stop and take the following oath on your own behalf.

I Pledge…

⟅ *I* will stop being offhanded about my life and neglectful of my well-being. I will learn to care about my self.

⟅ *I* commit myself to *knowing* and *understanding* the way my body, mind, and spirit work…and the effects circumstances and people have on me.

⟅ *I* will focus my concern on my self and pay attention to the things that bring me down. And I will patiently learn how to redraw the map of my life, learning new ways to move through depression, until I am consistently able to live with hope and happiness again.

⟅ *I* will remind myself—when I'm tempted to give up this effort—"My own self-care is vitally important to the life I want to live. If I'm not well, I'm less of the loving, giving person I want to be. If I'm not well, I can't enjoy this gift of life I've been given."

〜 *I* will affirm my value in God's eyes. Believing in my own intrinsic value is a powerful tool in my fight against depression.

〜 *I* will not allow my own past mistakes, or wrongs done to me, to hinder my future.

〜 *I* will seek the help I need until I am well.

If you are willing to make this commitment to your personal well-being, you have taken a bold first step out of your depression.

Oddly enough, many of us have never made a commitment like this before. Maybe we've thought we weren't worth the effort. Possibly we've thought we were indestructible. Maybe it doesn't seem heroic—it seems "selfish" or like "navel-gazing." What we've considered heroic is caring for the needs of everyone else around us—and acting as if *we* have no needs.

If you tend to think that way let me be the first to welcome you to reality. *To be human is to have needs.* And our task is to find out what we need for balance and well-being. When we commit to doing this, something happens.

Personal Miracles

The moment we assume responsibility for our own well-being, miracles take place.

Miracle #1 ✦ We sense a new kind of empowerment inside. Spiritual people recognize this power that comes from beyond our selves as "the power of *grace.*"

It's as if we've said, "All right, I'm ready to patiently examine the truth about my life. I'm willing to see the things that are 'nuking' me. And I'm willing to work to make whatever changes I need to make." And subtly…then more each day…we find ourselves in the company of a God who replies, "Good. Now that you're willing, I can help you."

Miracle #2 ⚓ By taking responsibility for our selves, we begin to develop a "supercapability"—we start to pick up on the sources of our trouble and defeat.

It's as if we've taken up a post as watchmen over our selves. We've given our eyes permission to open, we've become willing to see our lives more clearly. The new grace that's now with us empowers us with the gift of *insight.*

Gradually we begin to see the factors that conspire against us, sending us into depression. Not just the outer triggers, but the inner ones as well.

Eventually, as we gain the big picture perspective on our lives...plus insight into our responses to life's many opposing forces we can create a "map" that leads us through and out of depression.

Your Way Out

Take some time now to consider the different areas of your life. The checklist below can help you to become aware of trouble spots in your life, even some that would otherwise go unnoticed.

First go through the inventory on your own. Read the description after each entry, and check the spaces that apply to you.

Second, gain even more advantage over depression by going through the inventory again in the company of another person. This should be someone who knows you well. Someone with whom you can be absolutely honest—either a close friend and confidant, or a professional counselor. Give them:

- **The freedom to make honest observations...**without resisting or arguing with them. You don't have to agree with their assessment. But few things are more tiring than having someone ask for your help...then having them buck it every step of the way.

- **The right to challenge you if they think you're not being honest with yourself.** Caring requires both *support* and *challenge.* Value the friend or counselor who isn't a wishy-washy "yes" person. Value the man or woman who will be truthful *and* who will stick with you however long it takes for you to open your eyes and welcome the truth.

DON'T GIVE THIS JOB
TO THE WRONG PERSON

∼

You need to find your way through and out of depression. You don't need to be carrying someone else's concerns and needs while you work at this crucial personal task. There's time enough later to give attention to other people's needs. The life and well-being you're working on right now is your own. You don't need your space encroached upon by someone else's concerns.

For this reason, it will not work to go through this inventory with anyone whose sense of well-being and stability depends on your being "strong" and "well." Parents, spouses, and your children may have too great a personal stake in needing you to be "okay" for their sake. It's unlikely that they will be able to get beyond the way your depression makes them feel. (Threatened.) And so it's also unlikely they'll be able to help you recognize and gain insight into your own individual needs. If you've got a parent, spouse, or adult child who is independent, strong, and capable of doing this...you have a *gift!*

Never make any minor or dependent child be your emotional confidant. If you've already done this, go back and say, "I made a mistake in telling you about my emotional needs. When I did that, I asked you to carry a weight of responsibility you should not be carrying for me. You were great to listen and try to help me. I know you care *about* me. I care about you. That's exactly why it's important to me that you not try to take on the job of caring *for* me. *It's not your job.* Instead, I'm going to give the job of helping me work through my depression to an adult. That's what they're there for."

Say this in writing, in a thank-you note, if you need to.

With the following inventory in hand, invite your confidant to help you with the mapping process. You might help them understand what you're asking of them by saying: "I'm having trouble with depression. I need to tell you some things that are contributing to it." (Be ready to tell them what you checked on your first time through the list.) "And when I read the things I didn't check, tell me if you think I'm missing something."

· A PERSONAL WELL-BEING INVENTORY

What follows is not an exhaustive list of potential health problems. It's not meant to be used as a diagnostic tool or in place of an examination by a healthcare professional. It can be used, however, to help you become more aware of healthcare issues you haven't noticed, that require attention because they are contributing to your depression.

→ Major Factors

Certain major factors can contribute to depression, factors that are like earthquakes because they shake and unsettle us at the core of our being. They come as strikes against the foundations of our personal well-being.

Here's the thing about the great tectonic events of life. Sometimes we go through the shaking event pretty well. At first. But later, because life now has to settle into a new reality, all of us have to deal with the aftershocks. If the initial quake didn't do it, the aftershocks can still knock us down.

Consider the following major causes of depression. You may find it helpful to record a triggering event in the space provided. Have you experienced:

____*Major love loss.* Have you recently lost someone you love through death, or because an important relationship ended? Maybe the loss isn't so recent—maybe it's years old—but its deepest impact is just now hitting you. Have you been unable to find a compatible partnership? Have you awakened to a big disappointment in your intimate life?
I am lonely and grieving for _____
_____.

___*Major move.* Has a move caused you to cut close, daily ties with friends or family? Have you experienced the disorientation of a move? Have you had to do the tiring work of finding new doctors, schools, shopping, recreational facilities—not to mention putting out the effort of getting to know new neighbors?
I have lost familiar ties with _____
_____.

___*Major career setback.* Have you been forced to quit or transfer your schooling? Start a new college major? Do you feel stuck in your career, like you're going no place? Have you been passed over for promotion? Do you feel that you've never gotten the "break" you needed? Have you lost a job? Made a costly business mistake? Are you feeling vulnerable in your career because of age, gender, or educational level, or because of a bias against you?
I have been set back in my career by _____
_____.

___*Major financial setback.* Have you taken a huge hit to your income—planned or unplanned? Has this loss caused you to give up on certain dreams or goals? Forced you to give up free time or your preferred lifestyle, and take a (second) job in order to get by?
With the financial setback that cost me _____,
I also lost _____.

___*Major physical impairment.* Have you been diagnosed with a major or chronic illness? Have you been told you have a life-threatening illness? Has an injury cost you the ability to function in ways you took for granted? Has a physical limitation caused you to give up a favorite pastime?
My physical health has been affected by _____,
which has caused me to lose _____.

___*Major life passage.* Have you had a child leave home? Had a "milestone" birthday? Have you ended a commitment to a job, fellowship, service group, or other social affiliation? Have you experienced a transition in your religious beliefs? Are you feeling like you're in a "no-man's-land"…that time, a secure belief, or a cherished connection has slipped from your grasp? Have you crossed some invisible line in your life and feel disappointed that you haven't achieved a certain "something" by now?

I feel as though I'm losing _____,
and feel I may never have _____.

→ Filling in the Details

Here's where your commitment to self-care begins to meet the road. Over the next *week,* take time each day to consider the various aspects of your self and your life. You are looking for those "little" factors that add up to depression.

You are *not* in the business of finding someone to blame. (Put the gun down.) You are not looking for excuses. Because the various factors that contribute to depression can so easily remain hidden, you are simply setting aside a little time for important self-examination.

Depression and Your Body

Many of us are not in tune with our bodies. We're unaware of physiological sources of our depression. Other times, we're "too busy" or neglectful. Or we just want to deny we have a problem.

Sometimes women have an edge over men when it comes to body awareness because of their monthly cycle. Still, distractions like a hectic schedule and family demands can command our focus and keep us from noticing changes in our bodies. These changes can greatly affect our mental state.

Have you experienced any of the following:

___*Change in diet…or response to certain foods.* Our bodies often change without asking permission. A food we used to tolerate suddenly becomes a brick to the stomach. Food allergies and sensitivities crop up. Eating habits often have emotional connections, too. And changes disturb those connections. (Say a high point of your day was a meal with your spouse—and now your spouse is no longer there.)

I experience discomfort or changes in mood when I eat _____
_____ .

I feel (sad, empty, lonely, angry) when I eat under these circumstances: _____ .

___*Change in sleeping habits.* A new baby, an illness, an uncomfortable mattress, pressure on the job, worries about a child—many things can throw our sleeping patterns way off. Even carrying unresolved stresses to bed with us can wreck a good night's rest.
When I lay down to sleep I often feel _____ .
I get _____ *hours of uninterrupted sleep on average.*
I wake up at night _____ *times, and when I do I feel* _____ .
Most mornings I wake up feeling _____ .

___*Change in workload.* Has your workload increased on the job or at home? Were you handling a hefty load of work—but now age, illness, or just fatigue has run you down? Are you a habitual overworker because you'd rather do it yourself than train someone else? You're a perfectionist? You're afraid to ask for help? You're competing for a promotion or want a higher income?
I overwork (at home/work/elsewhere) because _____ .
I overwork by taking on these tasks: _____
_____ .

___*Change in overall health…or illness.* Sometimes changes in our overall health are subtle. Since our body is made up of numerous systems, take note of changes in your breathing, blood pressure, digestive and bowel habits, sexual functioning, menstrual cycle, and any joint or muscle discomfort. At other times, a chronic condition besieges us with new challenges. Both subtle and not-so-subtle illnesses greatly affect mood. Especially take note of exhaustion, tightness in the chest, difficulty breathing, radiating pains and numbness in your limbs, blurred vision, debilitating headaches, discomfort during intercourse, tenderness in certain areas, and strange tastes or smells that others do not experience.

I have experienced subtle, not-quite-right feelings in my ____
_____*.*
I experience chronic pain or inability to function in _____
_____*.*

___*Change in body chemistry.* Changes in body chemistry can be very subtle. Are you suddenly gaining or losing weight though your eating habits haven't changed? Do you experience sudden sweats, or anxiety? Cravings for certain foods? Is there a change in your body odor or the scent of your breath? A change in the color or texture of your skin? Color of stools or urine?
I have experienced subtle changes, including _____
_____*.*
I have experienced dramatic changes, including _____
_____*.*

Depression and Your Mind

A car is a wonderful thing…when it's working right. And a real pain in the neck when it's not. The same can be said for the brain.

Depression that originates inside your head comes from two sources. One is the brain itself, when its neural transmission pathways and chemistry are impaired. The second, and far more common, is what's inside the brain—that is, your *mindset.*

New studies have shown, interestingly, that what's *in* the brain—our thinking—can actually *shape* the brain. Later on, we'll look at this more closely and discover ways to reshape the mindsets that cause depression…with the wonderful side-effect that the brain itself is retooled.

But to begin, let's take inventory. Have you experienced any of the following?

___*Change in mental ability.* Focus was not a problem before—but now it is. You find you can't stay zeroed-in. During conversations, or while reading or watching television, your mind drifts. Communicating is a chore. People's names and other details escape you. Words won't come. Ideas aren't crisp. You just can't remember things.
I have trouble _____*.*

___*Change in mental restedness.* At the low-end of the scale, a restlessness or mild agitation comes over you. Or you feel anxious, and the atmosphere just feels "wrong." Maybe you are bothered by bad dreams, or when awake, by a sense that something terrible is about to happen. At the more pronounced end, you've begun to avoid certain things—like travel, going out, contact with certain things, places, or people. You have secret rituals—little things you have to do—to keep anxiety from overwhelming you.
My anxiety level is _____.
I experience anxiety when _____.

___*Change in mental "bouyancy."* Some of us are more naturally "up" people. Some are less so. But now you find yourself expecting more bad things to happen. You're more cynical about life or about people. You have a "so what" attitude, with little interest in doing something to help yourself when things go wrong. Or you feel powerless to help yourself. You often feel let down by other people—and you feel that if they don't care, why should you?
*I feel down about*_____
_____.
I have a very hard time feeling up because _____
_____.

___*Change in mental intensity.* You find yourself intensely focused on a person, an object, a goal, a pastime—to the degree that it's affecting your ability to live a balanced life. You have given up almost everything to pursue or nurture your obsession about this one thing. You can't seem to get it out of your head, even when you try to relax and change your focus. If you get it out of your thoughts, it returns later…and the intensity begins again. Losing, or not having, this thing would be your undoing, you think. Your intensity causes you to do things excessively, like phone, e-mail, or pray on the one hand…or to avoid these things totally on the other.
*I wish I could stop being overconcerned about*_____.
I'm afraid that if I stop thinking about it, the awful thing that will happen is: _____.
When I get obsessive about this, I _____.

___*Change in your mental "company."* When we're feeling good about ourselves and our thoughts, we don't mind letting other people into our thinking. We talk openly. Depression brings us "down" thoughts!—sometimes angry, blaming, or punishing thoughts. We may close down then, even shutting ourselves off from people close to us, because we don't want others to know how we're thinking. We don't allow them to "keep company" with us. (Oddly enough, we may open up more to strangers.)
*I don't want people to know I think about*_____
_____.
I don't share my depressive thoughts with _____,
because _____.

___*Change in your regard for life and living.* Depression affects our connection to life itself. Have you begun to think about limiting your life—by cutting yourself off from friends or favorite pastimes? Have you thought about ending your life?
*I have limited my enjoyment of life by*_____
_____.

Depression and Your Spirit

Your spirit is the part of you that holds your deepest values. It's the seat of your greatest passions, the fire of life that drives you. It's also the highest vantage point inside you, the point from which you view the world and give meaning to life's events. Your spirit is the aspect of your being that builds connections with the eternal and with God. It tells you about standards of right and wrong.

When our values are shaken, when our passions are crushed or denied…when life throws events at us that are confusing or too painful to grasp…when we have lost our connection with God… depression will be generated from our spirit and will spread into the rest of our being.

Taking inventory in your spirit, have you experienced any of the following:

___*Challenge to your values.* Once you had some kind of handle on what was important. Friendship and loyalty. Standing up for certain causes or principles. Fidelity and trust in intimate relationships. Now something has shaken your core values.

I once valued _____, *but that value was shaken by* _____
_____.

___*Challenge to your passions.* You've always had a dream. You've longed for it. Worked toward it. Now…reality has crashed in. The thing you've poured out your time and energy for is a dismal disappointment. Or something has blocked you, maybe even crushed your hope.
With all my heart I wanted _____,
but now my way is blocked by _____.

___*Challenge to your view of life.* When life makes sense, we feel "on top of things." But when the universe turns its darker side to us, we're left with confusion, chaos. When we ask "Why?" and no answer comes…then we're lost and unhappy.
I think life is bad because _____.
I think the world is an unfriendly, unhappy place to be because
_____.
I feel down and confused because I don't understand why ____
_____.

___*Challenge to your connection with God.* Maybe you've never had one…and you're suddenly uncomfortable about that. Maybe you feel abandoned or betrayed by God in a time of need. Or you've become angry and disheartened with God because people who represent God have been mean, petty, or disappointing. Possibly, someone has told you that God is definitely unhappy with you and doesn't want you around. (But how would *they* know that?)
I feel disconnected from God because _____
_____.

___*Challenge to your position with God.* When we violate a code—either the written one of our religion or the private one we've created—we tend to believe that God is unhappy with us Maybe that God has rejected us or is going to punish us. We may fear that God is going to hurt us, or someone we love, as a way to pay us back for our wrongdoing.

I think God is unhappy or angry with me because _____
_____.

I'm afraid God may punish me now by _____.

SOME CAUTIONS

This personal inventory is intended to help you recognize the sources of your depression and create a strategy that will help you walk out of it. There are a couple of cautions you should keep in mind, however.

Caution #1. Remember to use this inventory as a help—but not your only help—in getting a handle on where your depression may be coming from. I repeat, this is not a tool for self-diagnosis...but for self-discovery. It's possible your depression has a cause that you won't be able to locate on your own. Enlist the help of compassionate friends and caring professionals.

Caution #2. If there are a number of sources of depression in your life, your situation might seem overwhelming to you. You may think, "I'm never going to turn all this around. My life is a wreck."

STOP! What you are feeling is the downward-spiral nature of depression, as the negative energy of one trigger event pulls other aspects of your life into the depressive downdraft.

You do not have to turn your life around in one day, one week, or even one month. You do not have to "handle" every issue at once. In fact, once you've located key issues—or even the one key issue—that trigger your depression, other lesser issues will tend to work themselves out.

Now that you've taken inventory...don't add to your distress by going over and over all your troubles. It's time to shift your attention to solutions.

3

Freeing Your Head

*T*wo people are told they have the same serious illness. When Paul gets the news, he drops out of most of the activities he loves. He takes the fearful attitude that he doesn't want to add injury to illness. He focuses around the disorder until his life is a grid of timetables—doctor's appointments, medical tests, pill-taking, a support group. A conversation with him centers around complaints about his pains and discomforts, which are many and getting worse. You could say Paul is *illness-focused.*

Ask Paul how he's doing. "Other than being sick and in pain… just fine," he answers sarcastically.

Kayla takes a lot of the same actions as Paul. She hooks up with a good specialist, schedules ongoing medical tests, buys a plastic "pill minder" to keep up with her medications…but that's where the similarity ends. The difference is, Kayla takes the attitude that she wants to focus on "living well," given her diagnosis.

"I find ways around my physical limitations," she says. "I'm going to work through the boundaries of this thing as best I can and as long as I can."

Ask Kayla how she's doing. "You may not believe it—but the illness helped me focus on *living.* I'm doing new things I've always wanted to try, keeping active, and having the time of my life. Sometimes I go weeks without feeling the effects of the illness."

Paul and Kayla's medical tests turn up very similar results. But while Paul gets worse, Kayla says the pain is lessening. Paul is always exhausted, while Kayla says she has "enough energy to do pretty much whatever I want, if I pace myself."

Granted, many factors are involved when it comes to determining how well any one of us will do with a serious illness. But given that both Paul and Kayla are facing the same physical limitation—and the same potentially depressing situation—it seems obvious that *mental attitude* is playing a very important part in the way they are living.

What Do You Think?

Arguments rage back and forth among professionals about your head's role in depression. One side insists that depression is the result of *biochemical processes* in the brain. They want to treat the brain itself, with pharmaceuticals. The other side believes that the *way we think* is primary. Because how we think triggers the biochemical processes of depression. They want to treat the mind with various therapies. Both sides believe that making changes—in mental habits or in biochemistry—will actually help alter the brain itself.

Whether you're getting professional help of some kind or dealing with depression on your own, an important fact stands out: *What we think does matter. How we think affects our mood, and so determines the quality of our life.*

Depressed thinking is characteristically negative. Depressed thinking is "stuck" thinking, as witnessed by the fact that depressed people tend to rehash old arguments or replay sad, old memories of losses and "golden" times now lost. By observing depressed people and listening to them, all that becomes pretty obvious.

What's not so obvious—*especially* when we're the ones who are depressed—is that creating a positive attitude can actually help reverse the depressive spiral. This means we need to develop clear, ordered, forward-moving thoughts.

What follows are simple, effective strategies you can use to alter both the *way* you think and the *content* of your thoughts. Try these simple techniques and see which ones are most helpful in giving you a lift out of depression.

STRATEGIES FOR YOUR HEAD
Strategy #1: Give Your Thoughts "Air Time"

Depression can come from a "keep it to myself" attitude. From keeping a private store of bad, sad, angry, empty, hopeless thoughts.

From beliefs that are toxic. From ideas and perspectives that leave you in turmoil, inside or out, because they have no basis in reality.

None of us can see with perfect clarity when something is out of whack with our own way of thinking. The way we think is like the screen on a window. We look out at life…but unless we stop and make ourselves focus on it, we don't even notice the *screen*. But the screen actually blocks *some* part of our ability to see clearly.

Every one of us needs honest dialog with someone whose role is to listen closely as we give our thoughts "air time"—someone who can help us see when what's going on in our head is keeping us trapped in a depressive spiral. (After all, if we could clearly recognize this ourselves we'd stop, wouldn't we?)

Do this for yourself: Find a good counselor. This may be a professional counselor, therapist, or member of the clergy. Or it may be a wise and caring friend.

Finding a good counselor can be work. It's important to find the right connection and to feel comfortable that the counselor is right for you. Some people give up if they don't connect with a counselor on the first, second, or third try. *But do the work.* Investing some energy in your own self-care is actually a big part of moving toward well-being.

How will you know a good counselor when you find one? They will be:

- **Committed to sharing the load…but won't carry it for you.** This means they will offer objective opinions, observations, perhaps even positive suggestions. *However, they will not take over your decision-making role.*

    Look for someone who will let you unpack that burden of troubles you're carrying…temporarily. The idea is to give you a chance to take the pack of cares off your back so you can examine them. Why are you carrying them? Where did they come from?

    A good counselor will remember—and help *you* remember—that in every sense this is *your* pack. They can help you sort out which parts of the load are yours to carry, and which parts are not yours to carry. They will help you resettle your pack more comfortably on your adult shoulders. But a counselor isn't your dumping ground. It's not their responsibility to make choices for you or to do tasks for you. Like "deal with" your spouse. Or "straighten out" your troubled kids. Or tell you which job to choose. That work is yours and yours alone.

- **Safe.** A "safe" counselor is one who will not use you. This doesn't mean they won't charge you a reasonable rate for counseling. It does mean they will not use or abuse your need in order to gratify themselves emotionally, physically, financially, or spiritually.

  A counselor who's "safe" will hold everything you say in confidence. The only exceptions are when mandatory reporting is required by law, such as in cases of child abuse and sexual abuse; when your life or safety or someone else's is in danger; or when additional expert help is needed. A counselor should always inform you they are sharing information. There is no good reason for any counselor—be it a professional therapist, a clergyman, or a friend—to share your personal life without your consent.

- **Attentive.** A good counselor listens carefully to what you're saying. They won't assume they understand exactly what you mean. Instead they'll ask questions and repeat what they hear you saying. They will ask, "Is this what you mean?" "Is this how you feel?" "Did I get it right?"

  A counselor's first job is to understand you, even if it means fishing information out of you. So if you've got a counselor who, at the beginning, is asking questions more than offering answers and solutions—you've got a good one, not a bad one. (So don't make them fish. Help yourself by being open.)

- **Able to understand your feelings and perspectives.** A good counselor will work to see why you interpret life and events the way you do. They will give feedback like, "Okay, I think I'm seeing life the way you must see it. *Yikes!* No wonder you're depressed." In this way, a good counselor lets you know they're your companion, walking with you through this journey out of depression.

- **Able to help you face any "ghosts" or "monsters" in the attic.** When we were kids, we ran and hid from scary noises in the attic. What if it was something so big, so horrible, that we couldn't even look at it without shaking to pieces?

  Sometimes our depression comes from a belief that there is something so big, so horrible, hidden inside us that even looking at it will shake our life to pieces.

A good counselor isn't surprised, dismayed, embarrassed, or disgusted by our most "monstrous" self. They will recognize that we all tend to project our greatest fault or sin very large on the screen inside our head, then scare ourselves to death—like kids fascinated and horrified by an old monster movie on TV.

A good counselor is adept at spotting "ghosts" that haunt us from our past. Losses we haven't finished grieving. Duties we haven't discharged. Dreams we haven't given ourselves a chance to explore. They will recognize that, as long as we hide from those "energetic" parts of us, the parts that have any of our life in them, we will be haunted indeed.

A good counselor will help us to bravely open the door and will remain at our side as we explore the attic full of terrors, when this is the source of our depression.

- **Able to offer healthy challenges to your feelings and perspectives.** A good counselor will not say, "You're seeing this all wrong." That's discrediting and disregarding. It's not the kind of healthy challenge we need.

  A *healthy* challenge is one that offers us an *alternative way to view our situation*. After all, we all have limited viewpoints. And we can't think of every positive possibility or way out of our predicaments. A good counselor's role is to offer some creative alternatives.

  A word to the wise: Watch your own reactions when a counselor starts offering healthy choices. When we're not ready to work for healthy change we tend to complain, object, whine, blame, rehearse our wounds and losses again—just about anything to keep from making the changes, we need to make. *If you hear yourself putting up this kind of resistance…challenge yourself to work harder.*

- **Able to stick with you…even if you don't accept their views and advice right away.** A good counselor will be willing to stick with you while you test and try making changes to help yourself. They will even stick with you when you put up stubborn resistance to change. In fact, they may point out the fact that you are resistant, and ask if you feel it's worth it to continue meeting, given your resistance.

True, a counselor may recognize that you need a break… time to let your actions catch up with your thinking. They may also recognize that their ability to help you is at an end and that another counselor might be better for you.

Bottom line: They will stick with you…as long as you're willing to stick with the work yourself…and as long as you are able to make even "baby steps" toward well-being.

• **Able to say, "You're good to go."** A good counselor will recognize when the goal—health and independence—has been reached. They will recognize the day when you can do for yourself what they have been helping you to do. With a pat on the shoulder for congratulations, they will say, "Looks like our work together is done."

Strategy #2: Clean Up Your Thought Stream

Have you ever stopped to admire a beautiful mountain stream— only to notice it's been polluted with old tires, rusty cans, and paper and plastic litter?

Our thought flow is like a stream—constantly moving, fluidly rushing along—evaluating, judging, comparing. This running internal monologue is known as *self-talk,* and it can be a positive influence on our overall well-being when it's constructive and positive. But sometimes our self-talk can be as polluted as a junked-up mountain stream.

When our internal monologue is a flow of negative and destructive thoughts, it has a depressing effect on us. Do you recognize any of the following characteristics in your self-talk? If so, use these suggestions to "clean up" the polluting thoughts.

• *You are your own worst critic:* You evaluate your thoughts, words, actions, appearance—and decide that very little you do is right or acceptable.

You share your thoughts, and someone offers an opinion you judge to be more informed than yours. You think, "Man, what I just said made me sound *stupid.*"

Someone shows up in sharper clothes. You think, "I dress like a *slob.*"

A friend achieves a goal. You think, "I'm not that skilled. I'm pretty much a *dope.*"

Cleanup work: Put a stop to the name-calling. Put a stop to the negative comparisons that always leave you on the "down" side. Instead, speak to yourself in the positive. You might also want to use the opportunity to evaluate your response in a thoughtfully constructive way. Tell yourself:

"I was saying what I *thought* was true and accurate. This person has more information. Now I'm better informed."

"He looks sharp. Let me think—do I care enough about how clothes make me look to use them to make a statement about myself? Or do I want other things about me to identify who I am?"

"She's worked hard to reach that goal. Maybe she can tell me how to find the personal discipline so I can reach some of *my* goals."

- *You are your own judge and jury:* You vote on your status as a human being and return a "thumbs-down" verdict on your self.

  You make a mistake. You tell yourself, "I'm stupid."

  Someone ignores, forgets, or rejects you. You tell yourself, "I'm a loser."

  You admit you're depressed. You tell yourself, "I am one messed-up human being."

  Cleanup work: Stop labeling and condemning yourself. You are committing an offense against your own person, grinding your very being into the dirt. Instead of turning everything into an opportunity to imprison or punish yourself, evaluate the situation more objectively. Tell yourself:

  "I'm imperfect and I'm learning. And I made a mistake. That's how everyone learns. No big deal."

  "When someone ignores, forgets, or rejects me, that's a statement about who *they* are. Not about who *I* am."

  "Depression is a state I can learn to overcome. I'll be stronger, healthier, and more compassionate toward other people who are struggling after I learn how to get through this."

- *You hear only the worst:* You have selective hearing, and you strain out the positives—allowing only the negatives to get through.

A doctor tells you: "You have a condition that can be serious but—good news for you—we have tremendous success treating it." You hear: "…condition…serious."

A boss tells you: "You did a wonderful job on this project. A few changes and this could be even better." You hear: "…could be…better."

Cleanup work: Write down the whole truth, including both the negatives and positives you've heard. Focus on the positive by asking questions about what you can do to create the positive condition or get the best result. You have to think the situation over anyway—so focus your thoughts on the positive. Dwelling on a negative has never stopped it from happening. And when you aim for the best, you'll always land somewhere in the "better-result zone."

- ***You allow feelings to rule.*** Your unspoken motto is "I feel, therefore I am."

  Yes, we need to give room to bad and sad feelings. Denying them is a mistake. But feelings only need *some* room—not every bit of our interior space. After all, feelings are not facts. They are just feelings *about* the facts.

  Clean up work: Believe it or not, you can set a limit on the time you allow a negative feeling to hold sway. Depending on the weight of the event, you might say, "I'm going to give myself 10 minutes [or a day, a few days, a month, this season] to let this feeling work itself out."

  During the time you've allowed, take time to explore the feeling. At a minimum, ask yourself, "How am I going to deal practically with the situation or news that's triggered this feeling? What can I do now to get the best result, given what I have to deal with?" If you're overwhelmed or have no ideas, get someone's counsel.

  If the event you're dealing with is more major…a death, a career turnover, a grief, or depression of unknown origin…you will obviously need more time, effort, and strategies to explore and resolve the depressive feelings into positive new directions.

  Whether our depressive moods are triggered by things small or great, we do well to tell ourselves from the outset, "I'm going to explore this feeling as much as I need to… but my ultimate goal is to walk out of it and go on with a healthy life."

- *You allow someone else's bad mood to become a statement about you.* Some of us are way too sensitive to other people's feelings. We not only observe when someone is mad or sad, we think it always says something about *us.*

  Your spouse is sad or angry. You think, "I must have failed them somehow."

  Your kids are bored or in a cranky complaining mood. You tell yourself, "I must not be providing them with enough creative and positive things to do. I should have encouraged more good friendships."

  Someone acts pouty, as if whatever is bothering them is your fault. You think, "I wonder what I did wrong *this* time."

  Cleanup work: In reality, other people's moods don't have to trigger *any* big response from us. Their moods are *their* moods.

  When someone is going through a mood, we need to keep a healthy emotional distance and not take on their mood. *They* need to work it through. Often other people will try to get us to take on their mood—maybe just to share the misery!

  If someone wants to talk, let them talk. Everyone needs understanding, and we can simply say, "I can understand why you'd feel that way." Sometimes understanding is all that's needed—not help to "fix" the matter.

  If someone wants advice, give them any wisdom, insight, or practical suggestions you have—*once.* But if taking on other people's moods is a difficulty for you, you may also need to say, "I'm sorry, but I'm not able to help you with this right now. I'm working through some difficulties of my own, and I know it wouldn't be good for either of us."

  Tell yourself, "I need time to learn how to separate *their* moods from *my* moods, and not take on the negative emotions of others."

- *You jump to the worst conclusion.* It's very difficult for you to consider that things might *not* turn out badly for you.

  Your boss says, "Profits were down a bit this quarter." You think, *I'm going to lose my job. Then I could also lose the house. And my kid may have to drop out of college. And….*

Jumping to the worst possibility *amplifies* the negatives and helps our darker moods loom larger. Instead, it's time to become a "best-case scenario" kind of person. We cannot stop the worst from happening if it's going to. But we can always make choices as to how we'll respond.

Cleanup work: We can use our ability to "anticipate" outcomes as a *gift.* We can get creative and set up all kinds of scenarios that lead to positive outcomes for us.

We might tell ourselves: "This might mean longer hours, more work. But I like it here, so I'd better get ready for some short-term pressure from the boss."

Or we might say: "I am one of the lower people on the totem pole. I can get out my resume, put the word out quietly that I'm looking, and be well on the way to making a job change if it comes to that. I'll start calling contacts this weekend."

Or: "They *always* tell us profits are down just when bonuses and raises are supposed to be reviewed. My guess is that this management trend is going to continue." Again, you go to work on your resume and contacts.

- *You believe it's better to live with "sour" or "cynical" thinking.* Your bumper sticker reads: "Expect the worst. You won't be disappointed." You actually believe you're protecting yourself from disappointment by letting negative thinking rule your head.

  Someone tells you, "The stock market's up! The economy is good." You think: "Watch it. He's probably going to hook you into some investment scheme."

  A friend with a newfound or deep faith tells you, "Try praying (or meditating, or reading sacred writings, or attending worship services). I'm finding it helps for me." You think: "Sucker. Religion is for people who are easily misled."

  Okay, we've all had disappointments and have been deceived by fast-talking people. But mental instability, depression, and even mental illness can result from long-term sour thinking.

  Cleanup work: Sometimes we're soured on life because we made a bad decision and got sucker-punched. We might have asked more questions...but didn't. We might have gotten the promise in writing...but didn't. The healthy response to soured situations is *not* to become soured on life. It's to recognize that sometimes we will run into situations that can go sour. We can learn to make better agreements next time—whether in business, friendship, or love—in which the terms and expectations are clearer up front. And…

We can accept this truth about life: Sometimes we're going to win, and sometimes we're going to lose. We can't expect that every investment we make—financially, emotionally, physically, mentally, spiritually—is going to pay off. That's not realistic.

After every letdown we need to tell ourselves, "It's time to get back in the saddle and try again. I can use what I've learned to make better decisions. And now I'm better prepared inwardly to handle disappointments, which are just a part of life."

Something else: We've all heard of that famous "leap of faith." We all need to pick a time and place where faith is needed…and then launch out, trusting someone else for things over which we have no power.

Investigating anything by asking rational questions is absolutely necessary—whether it's a stock purchase or a spiritual faith. But after that, we need to make the leap…or at least take a step. We put our money down. We trust in what a spiritual friend tells us. We ask for God's help or guidance.

Absolutely everything we undertake in life requires adjustments. Deeper exploration. Re-evaluating. But one thing is sure: We never grow if we stay stuck in doubt and cynicism and never launch out in faith.

Strategy #3: Sort Out Mind Clutter

Too many details to keep straight. Too many goals to pursue. Just plain too much noise and confusion. Our heads can be like that junk drawer where everything gets tossed, until we have no clue what's important to keep and what should be thrown out.

"Mind clutter" wears us down with fatigue—often to the point of depression. We need time to sort out our thoughts and put life in order again. So, do this for yourself:

→ *Find other heads (and bodies) to handle those details.* Make lists of projects and work to be done around your home or workplace. Just because you know all that needs to be done, and in what order, doesn't mean you have to hold it all in your own head…much less *do* it all. Learn to delegate to others.

→ *Focus on one major goal, let lesser goals fall into line.* Imagine that your goals are like airplanes, circling in order, waiting to land at a major airport. Only *one* can be brought in to land at a time without risking a terrible pile-up.

You can become the air traffic controller of your own life. This means: Prioritize until you know the top goal you want to accomplish. The second. The third. Write a strategic plan and spread out your goals over time. Revisit your plan monthly or quarterly to revise it as necessary.

Strategy #4: Get into New Head Space

Introspective. Feeling closed in. Rehearsing unpleasant thoughts. These are all characteristics of depressive thinking. And they tell us we need to learn how to get into new, more open "head space."

Finding new head space means learning how to lighten up our thinking, alter our perspective, get out of the thought ruts where we're spinning our mental wheels deeper into depression. Maybe you've tried "getting away from it all" and that didn't help. That's because you went out to find new physical space…but took your same old head along with you. So, do this for yourself:

- *Choose a getaway place.* This can be as exotic as a trip to the islands…or as simple as a sitting on a quiet park bench in the sunshine. When we're depressed, simple is generally better. The point is to choose a spot where you can go to distance yourself from any factors that contribute to your depression. It can help if you create a firm mental barrier by asserting, "I'm leaving *behind* the things that are depressing me."

- *Focus on restful sights and sounds.* Nature, with its vibrant mix of colors, sounds, and shapes, has wonderfully restorative powers. Music from a portable CD or tape player can redirect our thoughts and mental patterns, lifting us up and out of down moods, inspiring positive feelings like wonder, joy, gratitude, beauty, playfulness. Avoid music that has an adverse effect on your emotions.

This combination of states—being physically at rest while mentally attuned to natural sights and sounds—has a positive and lifting effect on the mind and spirit. If you want to do something a little more active with your thoughts…

- *Play the game "What if…?"* What if…we could get beyond any limitation in our life? What barrier would we move beyond? What unfulfilling duty would we leave behind? Or…what if we could change something in order to help us find fulfillment where we are? "What if…?" is a great way to help us think beyond the boundaries that seem so real, immovable, and limiting.

  Maybe you've become depressed by telling yourself, "I can't finish my college degree until the kids are in school full-time…but the baby's only 16 months old." Or "I'd love to switch jobs, but…"

  Every time you hear yourself say "but"—check yourself for "impossibility thinking." Instead, turn your mind toward positive, possibility thinking. Set your head in a new direction with thinking that begins with "But what if there *is* a way?"

Strategy #5: Get into Someone Else's Head

Sometimes depression comes from dwelling like a hermit inside our old and limited perspectives on life and living. We have become trapped in thinking and views…long after they have become life-draining. That happens when we are:

- too strongly attached to living by laws and rules

- holding on to an image of "the way we want things to be"

- rigidly trying to make our or someone else's life work out according to a "script"

Escaping depression may require us to learn how to *enlarge* our thinking. One way to do this is to open up to others' viewpoints. This can benefit us when we're feeling negative about our own lives. It can also benefit our relationships with others when we're feeling down about them. So do this for yourself:

- *"If you were me…"* If we suspect our depression may be coming from "trapped" and too-rigid thinking, we can ask for time to dialog with other people who are most definitely not like us. We

GET INTO THE FLOW

~

One characteristic of depression is "trapped" thinking. We can't get old thoughts out of our head. We go around and around with old solutions that don't resolve our problems, and we can't imagine new solutions to make our lives any better. Depressed thinking is like sluggish, murky brown water caught in an eddy at the edge of a slow river.

One characteristic of healthy, positive thinking is that it "flows." It's flush with new ideas. Its hopeful outlook quickly sweeps away the sediments of negative thinking and despairing attitudes. "Flow thinking" is like the strong, steady, buoyant, self-cleansing current of a healthy river. There are different ways to express "flow" thinking—for example, by journaling or by praying.

The important characteristics of "flow thinking" you will want to cultivate are:

- *Swim "sans accoutrement."* We are talking about a purely private indulgence here. Take the attitude that no one else is ever going to listen in. If you are journaling, keep it absolutely to yourself. Now, setting aside all shyness and embarrassment…

- *Dive in.* Learn to "get into" your own thoughts by asking, "What *do* I think about this?" Parroting other people's thoughts without giving attention to our own opinions is a downer. Gently turn aside even good ideas that came from other people by asking, "What does *my* experience tell me?"

- *Ride the currents.* Don't censor any thought. Let your ideas come freely. Negatives, criticisms…let it come. And by all means…positives, insights, and creative solutions. Ride the currents now; sort them out later as you need to.

- *Watch for "new currents."* Often, people who are experiencing "flow thinking" find that a "new voice" begins to speak—bringing wisdom and solutions that seem to come from beyond themselves. *Watch for this to happen to you!*

Getting into "flow thinking" has a remarkable way of bringing us a sense of mental renewal. It can bring about a powerful, mood-altering affect, lifting us up from a depressive mindset.

don't always need an "expert." Most of us have everyday, easy-going, upbeat, free-spirited, soul-at-ease kinds of people in our lives.

We can say, "Here's the situation I'm in, as I see it. But help me out here. How do *you* see it?" We might discuss not only our position but our strategy—the way we're trying to work things out. We can ask, "Am I going about this in a way that's defeating me?"

Of course we're not asking this person to make decisions or changes for us. And we're not asking them to work out whole strategies for rearranging our personal world. That's our job. But learning to look at our lives from an outsider's viewpoint can act like an ice-breaker in the Arctic when our mental processes are frozen in the grip of depression.

- *"Tell me what it's like to be you."* When we're feeling down because someone else isn't living according to our high hopes and wishes for them, we can do ourselves and them a huge favor by learning how to "shelve our script" for them.

  How do we do this? We ask them questions that get us out of *our* heads and into *theirs.* Things like: "Tell me what you think about—what you hope and dream about. Tell me what makes you happy." In a conflict, we can ask, "Tell me how you see this situation," and "What would you do to resolve it?"

  What we're really asking is, "Tell me what it's like to be you." This conveys a profound respect for the other person, and it opens up their thinking for us…which also opens up our own.

  Learning to see someone else's life from *their* viewpoint can be an amazing thing—especially if something they're doing is triggering "down" thinking in us. Getting into their head can help us recognize and let go of ideas and goals we have for them—the ways in which we're not likely to change them, no matter how much we pressure or try to influence them. We can then recognize points of agreement we might build on. It can also help us learn how to support them as they create their *own* life—not the one we imagine they should be living.

  In either case, our new understanding can set us free from the depression generated by futile thinking that's not based in reality.

Strategy #6: Make Decisions...and Go in Peace

Indecision can be a cause of depression. Failing to make decisions...or making and unmaking them over and over...turns our mind into a wheel spinning deeper into mental mud.

Let's be clear. We do *revisit decisions* when we've received new information or insight about a situation. At such times we may decide to reverse or change our course slightly. This is just being smart and flexible, and it's not what we're addressing here.

Indecision is when we make and *remake* choices...without ever setting out in the direction of our choosing. Indecision is the endless weighing of pros and cons...without ever moving ahead in reality. So do this for yourself:

• *Make a list of values.* Our strongest decisions come when we base them on strongly held values. Sometimes, though, we find we are stuck over a decision because two values are in conflict.

For instance, we may feel stuck in a relationship and find ourselves getting more negative and depressed all the time. We say we value *commitment,* so we stay in the relationship.

Then on another day, we decide we value *honesty,* or *thoughtfulness,* or *emotional intimacy*—and our decision is to move on. Or perhaps we feel unfulfilled and down about our career, but we value *security* today...only to shift tomorrow and want more *authority,* or more *money,* or more *creative freedom.*

We do ourselves a huge favor by taking the time and effort to know which values we rank highest and which we rank lowest. Being clear about the values we hold highest...and those we care about least...is a first step in strong decision-making.

• *Let go of the myth of "The Perfect Decision."* Stop procrastinating, believing there will come a better time or better conditions that will help you make "the perfect decision." This side of heaven, the perfect *anything* will rarely be our lot.

• *Decide...and go for it.* When we set off on the highway of our own plan, we can expect a new kind of energy to help move us along. We can also expect this momentum to offer us an upward lift out of the depression that's resulted from spinning our wheels.

- *Remain flexible.* Once we're up and moving again—*this* is the time to remain *flexible.* That doesn't mean we let the first hint that things aren't going smoothly take the wind out of our sails. It *does* mean we stay alert to challenges and keep thinking our way around problems. It means continuing to re-evaluate our progress, so we can recognize when a seeming "detour" actually becomes the best way for us to go. Flexibility can mean recognizing that another value that has been way down on our list suddenly needs to rise closer to the top.

Joan lived in mild depression for years, dreaming about a business of her own, highly prizing the chance to *benefit from all the profits* instead of being a wage-earner, and also the chance to be *self-determining.* Finally, she launched her business—*her* baby.

A year later she recognized she was likely to fail if she didn't add a partner to help with aspects of the business in which she was very weak. *Cooperation* had not been on her list of values at all when it came to this dream. But she was savvy enough to let it rise to the top, and she kept her dream from being derailed by a business disaster.

Strategy #7: Refuse to Go Back Over Old Ground.

Few things are more depressing than going over...and over...and over...the past, in a negative mindset.

Some of us play the sad game, "Name Those Regrets." We tell ourselves:

"I should have married that other guy/woman."

"I should never have had kids at such a young/old age."

"When I had the chance, why didn't I buy into that business?" or "...get that higher degree?" or "...make that career move?" or "I should have taken my child to the doctor sooner" or "...not listened to the doctors."

We drive ourselves deep into depression, imagining life as it *might have been.*

Some of us also play that other sad game, "They Did Me Wrong." We remind ourselves:

"My best friend betrayed me. Kicked me when I was down."

"My employer dumped me, after years of hard work and loyalty."

"My spouse cheated on me."

THINK ABOUT "BETTER" THINGS

∽

"Mind candy" describes the thoughts we use to amuse, distract or thrill ourselves. Unfortunately, some of us live on mind candy…and a steady diet that has depressing effects.

How *is* your mental diet? In your reading and music-listening, do you take in a lot of dark, depressing, degrading, or despairing ways of looking at people, yourself, or life?

If what you're feeding your mind brings "down" thinking:

✦ *Switch reading material.* If you're into reading books with heavy themes…switch. Try something inspirational. Read biographies of saints or heroes—men and women who lived for ideals. Check into inspirational and motivational writings.

✦ *Switch off the TV for a while…a good, long while.* How much of real life are you missing by watching too much television? Especially avoid the raunchy. No matter how much you may argue that it's your right to watch and that we live in a free-speech culture, raunch brings us and our view of life *down*.

✦ *Switch "brands" of music.* Music has a power to go deep and have strong effects—as much or more than images we watch. If your music-listening is, like your viewing, on the depressing, degrading, or raunchy side… *switch.* Tune in to music that makes you glad to be fully alive.

Too often we use the past as an excuse for not being fully alive today.

Do this for yourself: Learn to live in the present. Nothing can alter the past…but the way we treat our past affects our present. This means we must learn *how* to treat the past when our memories are the source of depression. Here are some suggestions:

· *Treat past experiences like a movie.* We choose our video viewing depending on the mood we want to put ourselves in. When old depressing scenes begin to roll, we can hit the "stop" and "eject" buttons. It's well within our power to say, "I'm not going to watch that old 'footage' again." And then "shelve" the depressing memory.

- *Treat our past self with respect.* If we could have known what yesterday's choice would bring…if we could have chosen perfectly…if we could have seen through our own weaknesses…we might have chosen differently. But we acted on what we knew to do *then* without the experience and insight we have *now.*

- *Treat our past errors with generosity and mercy.* Saying "Look what I did wrong" teaches nothing. Saying "Look at all I've learned from what I did wrong!" teaches us how to live better today.

- *Treat past emotions…with care.* Memories trigger emotions that can be very intense—as real as the first time we felt them. Revisit old emotions like anger, sadness, or fear *only if you are ready to work through them, resolve them, and go on.*

Learning to live in the present also means learning how to treat today. Here are some suggestions:

- *Focus today on the "current."* Think of your life as having an ever-renewing quality…like a stream or river. Create an attitude of alert "expectancy"—looking for the good, pleasant, fun, interesting things that will come your way today.

- *Focus on letting go of problems and hurts quickly.* As today's "current events" carry difficulties and problems your way, make it a policy to deal with them as quickly as possible… and let them go. Don't internalize and "store" them for later.

- *Focus tonight on tomorrow.* Before bedtime, make it a habit to revisit the day and put its issues to rest. Maybe that means having a conversation or writing a note. Maybe it means journaling or praying. In these ways, you can "put to bed" the day you've just lived…. And *then* you can briefly refocus on the needs and challenges that lie ahead tomorrow. The result should be restful sleep followed by energy and enthusiasm in the morning.

4

Lifting Your Spirit

Possibly you were ready to skip over this chapter. If so, it's probably because popular thinking doesn't give much value to "spirit." The word itself sounds vague, airy, indefinite.

Most of us don't understand the central role our spirit plays in our life—including its utterly crucial role in determining our total well-being and quality of life. We may think of spirit only in terms of pep-rallies, or sales conferences where our boss is trying to get us to "rah-rah" the latest company goal. If we think of spirit in religious terms, we might link it with (think with a deep voice here) SERIOUS matters like "holiness"—or from a contemporary mindset, we may associate spirit with "juiced-up" church services of the electric-guitar-and-drum-set variety.

To our loss, we don't associate well-being of spirit with physical, emotional, or relational well-being. Is it any wonder then that we overlook our spirit's vital role in freeing ourselves from depression? Often we settle for "coping strategies," when something much better is available—a way to move out from under, a way to escape the crushing weight of depression.

Fires and Fish

We've seen that the mind can be a great hindrance...or a great help in relieving depression. But there is a level of being deeper than our mind. At the core of our being lives our spirit.

Our spirit is the seat of our innermost drives. It's energized by our desires to live, love, and act according to our values. Thus our spirit is the power center of our whole life. It constantly energizes our thoughts and actions. Interestingly, our spirit has two aspects.

One aspect can be recognized by its brilliant sparks of inspiration, desire, and will. This part is readily visible...as the light in our eye, the spring in our step, the choices we live by. The other

51

aspect is murkier, not clear to us—like a slow dark current where not-quite-formed motives and wishes lie like bass under fallen logs, gathering the strength to leap up into daylight and surprise us.

Many of us ignore our spirit because we're busy dealing with the pressing demands we face every day. But our spirit has enormous power and is constantly at work in our lives. How so?

Someone gives you a chance to have your dream of a lifetime...and a great energy thrills every fiber of your being. That's your spirit.

Someone you trusted and confided in betrays your secret...and the same great energy erects barriers against them...or lobs fire-bomb words at them. That's your spirit.

Someone you love needs you very much...and yet right now you're also being given a chance to reach a goal you've worked toward forever...and that energy within you is thrown into turmoil as one valued thing competes against another for your time and attention. That's your spirit.

We need the ability to recognize when depression is originating in the deep core of our being. We also need to learn how we can free ourselves from its crushing weight. In order to get an understanding of the important—and highly rewarding—task we're learning here...take a moment to let yourself "walk" through the following scenario.

PICTURE YOURSELF

There are a number of ways to picture the human spirit. One way is to imagine it as a seedling that's destined to grow into a tree. Take a moment and...

～ *Picture yourself as a seedling...*

A seedling begins green and tender. If you are allowed to grow freely, without interference, you will naturally become a tree of strength, dignity, and beauty. You will develop outer thickness for protection. Also interior rings of intellectual and emotional growth for strength and endurance. And at a deeper level still, you'll develop another inner ring—your spirit—that will remain tender and supple, supporting new life throughout the whole structure.

❧ *Now switch the scene and picture yourself...*

> ...walking in a wooded area. You come across a heavy stone. Poking out from under its edge is the green tip of a seedling. Who knows what this small shoot might grow to become. A flowering ornamental. An apple tree. A great oak.
>
> Right now the stone's weight is bending this tree down. Keeping it from becoming what it was created to be. Under such pressure...without enough light or water...without the chance to move and grow freely...this tender shoot is struggling just to make it.
>
> Reaching down, you remove the weight.
>
> You have forever changed the life course and the destiny of this tree.

What's That Load You're Carrying?

Spiritual depression comes when we've been trying to carry great weights that our inmost being can no longer lift. Because spiritual issues can rest so deeply inside us that we fail to see them, we can benefit from a little careful self-examination.

Here is a short list of weights that may be stifling your spirit. Which can you identify in yourself? (It may help you zero-in on your range of needs if you *rate* them. Check the ones that apply, and also check how great a load it lays on your spirit.)

____*Emptiness.* We call it emptiness, but that hollow feeling is really more of an inner numbness that comes from other more hard-to-face sensations like *rejection, abandonment, meaningless-ness*...each of which can press down like a great weight on our spirit.

  ____*No Sense* ____*A Little* ____*A Lot* ____*Overwhelming*

____*Lack of hope.* Life's events can seem overwhelming. Sometimes our circumstances are tough. We look for change, relief, a better day...and it's too long in coming. We feel hopeless. At other times we feel saddled with too many burdens. We feel trapped because we think we have to carry responsibilities that are not ours, or because we're just carrying so many duties we can't possibly lift them all alone without help. Then our spirits sag beneath the weight until we sink.

_____*No Sense* _____*A Little* _____*A Lot* _____*Overwhelming*

___**Lack of purpose.** Without a goal or vision, we feel at loose ends, like we're headed nowhere. When we lack spark, drive, or motivation, we feel listless and without a reason for being. Even a sense that we're wandering or "not on track" weighs us down.

_____*No Sense* _____*A Little* _____*A Lot* _____*Overwhelming*

___**Guilt.** When we've done something wrong, the memory of it sits like an anvil inside. Actually, guilt can be real—tied to something we've done—or imagined—tied to a fear that we've offended. We can violate a formal religious code—say, by lying, stealing, dishonoring, or cheating. We can also violate our own personal code by not doing what our ethic tells us is right. Seeing ourselves as wrongdoers is a difficult weight to bear.

_____*No Sense* _____*A Little* _____*A Lot* _____*Overwhelming*

___**Lack of worth.** The weight of chronic low self-esteem is one of the most widespread of the spiritual "heavies." Maybe we feel we're not worth the time, effort, or attention of someone who's very important to us. Maybe that someone is God. We can't understand why our prayers aren't answered, why our plans and dreams always seem blocked. Believing that hardship and disappointment come our way because God is doling out blessings and favors to people who are more liked, more worthwhile…this lays a boulder on the spirit.

_____*No Sense* _____*A Little* _____*A Lot* _____*Overwhelming*

___**Shame.** When we can't measure up to the rules, demands, or expectations of other people we feel weak…not good enough… even defective. We may sense we've let other people down— maybe even let God down. Sensing we're a disappointment to someone else sets a heavy load on the spirit.

_____*No Sense* _____*A Little* _____*A Lot* _____*Overwhelming*

___**Condemnation.** Some of us feel like we've committed the unforgivable crime. What we did can't be undone—it's too late for that. Now we feel we're "marked" in some way, and if other people can't see that mark, we can…and God can. Maybe someone we love, or a religious figure, has told us that what we've done is unpardonable…or maybe we've just taken it upon ourselves to judge ourselves before anyone else has the chance.

_____No Sense ____A Little ___ A Lot ____Overwhelming

___*Despair.* Some of us find ourselves slipping into a dark zone that lies out beyond hopelessness. A voice tells us our situation will never turn around. In those moments, the light pretty much goes out. *This voice is a lying voice.* Mortals that we are—unable to see tomorrow—we are in no position to say that help and relief will never come.

Despair is a serious spiritual condition. If you are suffering from it, you should seek help until you find the right doctor, counselor, or clergyman to assist you.

_____No Sense _____A Little _____A Lot _____Overwhelming

___*Unforgiveness.* Perhaps we don't think of unforgiveness as a spiritual weight, one that contributes to depression—but it's one of the heaviest. Words of ancient wisdom tell us that spending our time judging, resenting, or seeking to punish gives us a "heart of stone." It leaves us dragging a heavy weight…like a prison ball around the ankle…ironically punishing *us* more than the one(s) we won't forgive.

Take time with this one. Call to mind anyone you've criticized, cut off, judged, looked down on, held in contempt, or condemned as being beyond help.

_____No Sense _____A Little _____A Lot _____Overwhelming

Once we begin to recognize the weights that crush the life out of our spirits, we need a plan. There may be a number of "stones" to remove. It's likely to take a little time. But we do need to lift the burdens off. By doing so we create a space and freedom so our spirit can gain strength, begin to grow healthy, and thrive again.

STRATEGIES FOR OFFLOADING DEPRESSION IN SPIRIT

Strategy #1: Get Closer to God

At the root of much depression lies disappointment…and often anger.

Sometimes these emotions are directed vaguely out at the cosmos. *Life...or the universe...has treated us badly.* Sometimes we feel let down or betrayed by God. *Why didn't God stop X from happening? Why didn't God make Y happen?*

Nationally acclaimed psychologist William Backus, author of *The Hidden Rift with God,* says that a vast number of clients he sees for depression carry some measure of disappointment or anger at God. Some are well aware they are furious that God did not help them at some moment of vital need. But many are lifelong church members—"good people"—who cannot admit they are raging inside because they have felt oppressed and overworked or let down, neglected, and abandoned by God.

So...if our spirit is telling us that God is the problem, the "source" of our anguish...how will getting closer to God help us out of depression?

This strategy, like the ones that follow, is better understood in the doing of it. That's because understanding something at the level of the spirit comes only by direct experience. You've got to live it to get it. Try these steps:

- *Ask God to become real to you.* Maybe you have a functioning relationship with God. Maybe you don't. Now is the time to renew that connection and take it to another level, or to start it up for the first time. Fortunately, saints, mystics, and ordinary spiritual people alike all assure us that God is no slouch when it comes to making an entrance. Given half a chance, God has no difficulty opening up new insights and bringing relieving solutions...even to dark and troublesome issues like depression.

  What you want to do is issue the invitation: "God, you have my permission to make yourself known to me in any way you can." That's pretty much it. But then be ready.

  Ready for what? As one of history's great "soul doctors" has said, God becomes present to us "by the most ordinary and subtle means." Those who believe God to be very real know the boundlessly creative ways God connects with people. So be ready for God to connect with you

  - in a dawning awareness within
  - with wise or directive words spoken by another person
  - by suddenly turning an event, miraculously, on its heel

A word to the wise on this "getting close to God" business:

"I keep asking God to change my circumstances, and nothing happens," says a 19-year-old who is dealing with disappointment and depression. "First God has to change things. *Then* I'll know this is a God I *want* to be close to."

Putting conditions on God by saying, "You do *this* and then I'll do *that*"…well, that would get our connection with the divine off to a wrong start. That would place us in the "God-seat" giving directions, wouldn't it?

Instead, just give God an open *invitation.*

- **Ask God to give you a bigger view of your life.** Many times depression comes from the feeling that we're trapped, locked in to a set of circumstances that we don't want. Too often our spirits wrestle and wrangle, trying to control and change people and situations. But many times life throws obstacles in our way that we can't change. It's a condition of life on this imperfect planet. Still, those obstacles need not block us. It's been said that when God closes all the obvious avenues that we wish to travel, we will instead be lead through a hidden way, one previously unknown to us.

Here's a meditation you can use:

~ *Picture your life as a map lying open on a table. You wanted to get from Point A to Point B with as little trouble as possible. (Don't we all?) Now something…or someone…has made your journey hard, or even seemingly impossible.*

~ *This is the point of frustration and discouragement for you.*

~ *Ask God to show you a new way to your destination. Or even a new destination. Allow God to reroute you…even to redraw the "map" of your life…as necessary.*

Another word to the wise: Every map has a "key." And *flexibility* is the key to following the map of every life.

When we learn to be redirectable when necessary, the miraculous happens. We usually discover that roadblocks and limits are not dead-ends after all. But first we must stop ramming our head into the barrier that keeps us from going in the direction we wanted to go. Then we can accept that the problems that block our way are really like the walls of a maze, redirecting our energies down new paths we would never have taken before. The secret lies in taking this new perspective…and then in taking even one small step in a new direction. Eventually, one step at a time, the new path *will* open. Guaranteed.

By learning to accept that life's most important directions come to us one day at a time, one step at a time, we actually stay more open and connected to God and to guidance.

Strategy #2: Get Honest

Depression at deep core levels can come from feelings we just don't want to admit. Maybe we're afraid that others or God will be unhappy with us for thinking and feeling certain things. Maybe we're heavily invested in seeing ourselves as "good," "strong," "nice," or even "holy," and this is keeping us from being able to see ourselves as normal. ("I'm a spiritual person, I can't be full of anger." "I should have more faith and not be afraid.") Maybe we think God will punish us by leaving us or taking someone we love away from us if we express our true thoughts and feelings.

Admitting we have negative emotions like fear, anger—even rage—means we're human. Admitting to others and confessing to God that our own choices and lifestyle have contributed to our depression means we're human, too. Nothing more. Unfortunately, many people are trained in youth to put on an "agreeable" face…no matter what they're feeling inside. We're trained to be "nice," not honest. But nice can have a price: *depression.*

The first step in working through any negative feeling is to let it out of its cage within our spirit into the free light of day. Only then can its power to harm us from within be transformed into productive energy directed into creative responses.

Strategy #3: Get Quiet

On one hand, we have the need to talk and offload the weights that lie heavy on our spirit. On the other hand, we need to cultivate interior space—an open and expectant attitude within—where new

GET IT OFF YOUR CHEST—CONFESS

As the old saying goes, "Confession is good for the soul."

Confession is about owning up to wrong we've done...and also owning up to the good we've left undone. (But if you think you're somehow the world's worst sinner, here's news: Stand in line behind the rest of us.) Confession is also a great way to let out those depression—inducing feelings that are stalking around in that "cage" deep inside you.

Here are some simple but important *dos* and *don'ts* of confession:

1. *Do* open your soul to someone who will keep your secrets secret. *Don't* try this with a person who your negative feelings are aimed at—they'll be too involved (and defensive) to offer the spiritual help you want.

2. *Do* find someone who will allow you to feel exactly what you feel until you're ready to move on. *Don't* hang around if their main response is: "You shouldn't feel depressed," or "Just trust God" (or some other bumper sticker slogan).

3. *Do* be as honest as you can be. *Don't* weaken your confession by making excuses for yourself or anyone else. Take your own part, speak the truth as you see it. Own your feelings of sadness, anger, or fear just as they are.

4. *Do* find someone who can stick with you for the long haul. In time you will want to move on from the negative feelings that are now triggering your depression. *Don't* be eager though. If we give negative emotions lots of sun and fresh air, they *will* change of their own accord.

5. *Do* be open to challenge. As a balance to number 2, we all need to be challenged if we are unwilling to face the truth, or if we're unwilling to move past the negative. The goal of honesty is not to wallow in our present state or bad feelings. We may need to be challenged to get professional help, to use pharmaceuticals, or to take a different approach to our problem. *Don't* run away when your confessor offers honest insights about you that are uncomfortable to hear!

6. *Do* remember that the person you are confessing to is not God. They are not perfect. They cannot make decisions and changes for you. *Don't* forget that you can ask God to bring wisdom and healing through this human vessel.

directions and answers can not only dawn, but grow. Creating this interior space requires two things: *quiet* and *solitude.*

Some of us find quiet and solitude disturbing, and so we tend to avoid them. Alone and quiet, we feel isolated. Or we experience a rising sense of desolating emptiness or guilt, or sadness, or remorse, and we fear we might be overwhelmed. Or we feel restless, bored—like we're "wasting time." And anyway, we're quickly distracted by demands from without and maybe some accusing voices from within. So we give up and do what everyone else does. We fill our lives with people, with busyness…and with the constant "sound-track" of a television, radio, or CD player.

To those of us who press through these first interior lines of resistance, quiet and solitude offer huge benefits. They become an essential part of our total well-being. Inwardly, we discover a still point…a strong, stable, and serene center. We learn how to live with perspective and balance as we encounter life's turmoil, insanity, and "wild pitches." We also experience benefits to our physical health. And we gradually create a spiritual space inside where we can actually "step apart" from conditions like depression. We learn that *we* are not our *depression* and that *it* is not *us.* And so we're no longer overwhelmed by it.

At the very least, quiet and solitude have restorative qualities to the spirit. Follow these simple, practical steps:

- *Choose a quiet time…and a solitary space.*

    Time. Early morning…midday…late at night…whenever you're at your focused best, pick that time. Stick to it. Building anything takes patience and commitment. Think of this as time spent building a shelter for your spirit. If you want a good sturdy one, it will take time.

    Space. You don't need to have a monastery or a pristine wilderness next door. All you need is a place that's solitary. A room where no one will disturb you. A bench on a porch, in a garden, or park.

- *Clear your inner atmosphere.*

    Confession is an essential part of clearing our interior space (see page 59). Confession helps remove the many guilts and regrets that preoccupy us when we need time and space for healthy interior growth.

Recollection is another ancient spiritual practice that also helps us clear our interior space. It is the business of helping our spirit get disentangled from all its everyday interactions with the stuff of life, the interactions that place so many demands on us that we wind up feeling "scattered" and "pulled apart." (Imagine yourself trying to rein in a team of wild horses all pulling in different directions and you'll recreate the spiritual stress put on, say, the average man or woman today.)

Practically speaking, here's what to do: Keep a little notepad at hand. Use this to write "memos" to yourself, reminders about the day's details, so they'll stop nagging you. Also keep a bigger pad or journal handy. Use this to capture thoughts and insights that come both *before* and *after* you get still. (After stillness in spirit, the mind can be unusually active.)

- **Settle into stillness.**

  A simple start-up technique is to focus on your breathing. Close your eyes. Relax. Breathe in slowly through your nose, and release as normal. Notice the wavelike rhythm. Eventually, let yourself notice the silence beyond your self…the stillness behind all noise and busyness.

  Focus on the stillness. For some of our poor spirits, this is the only time they get to let go of their load. Even at night we can carry the weight of unsettled emotions and events, into our dreaming. If you do nothing but feel rested and refreshed at a deeper level than ever before, this will be good enough for now.

- **Remain alert.**

  No, you're not likely to hear an audible voice or see heavenly lights. You *are* likely to experience flashes of insight, maybe even a sense that you are not abandoned to struggle through depression on your own.

  Learning to be still and listen—to open ourselves to insights from beyond ourselves—goes a *very* long way in helping us walk out of spiritually based depression. This is true when depression arises from the sense we're cut off or abandoned. Or that God is cold and uninterested in our needs, dreams, and goals.

Nothing could be farther from the truth. A true life of faith may include a sojourn in depression…but it will also include a time of moving *through depression* to a new and healthier place.

Strategy #4: Learn to "Pray into Action"

An important strategy has been intentionally left until now.

Spiritually based depression often comes from a deep sense of *hopelessness.* A situation is overwhelming, and we can't imagine how to change it. Our depression may come from living in the rut of *passivity.* Someone else—God, other people—is supposed to do it all. Or our depression may come after years of being overbearingly controlling. Believing *we* are supposed to do it all.

After learning to be still and listen…comes prayer. That means learning how to have an ongoing dialog with God, one in which we learn to balance *listening* with *talking*…and *acting.*

Some of us act first…and pray later. We get out on a limb, saw it off…and yell for God to catch us. Our depression comes from blaming God and the whole world for letting us splat on the ground when the free fall was our own doing.

Some of us pray…but it goes something like this. We hand God a long "To-Do List." Or we grind out "form" prayers. Or we build up anger, fear, sadness…until it's a depressing load…then we just *unload* in God's ear. This kind of praying—if that's even what it is—is more like a little kid dumping all his responsibilities on a "big person" and walking away. When we pray this way, we perpetuate a sense of helpless immaturity in ourselves. We become passive and overdependent, and leave ourselves wide open to depression.

Prayer is meant to connect us with *direction*…with *practical, real steps we are to take in the work of resolving the issues of our lives.*

To get a right sense about "praying into action," imagine having a *dialog* with an adult friend. You trot out your thoughts, opinions, worries. You raise issues. You talk out strategies you mean to use in handling problems. Then you wait for *feedback.* You hope for wisdom, perspective, some practical advice…and a dose of encouragement. Possibly even an offer of help.

But in the end, our lives are…well, *our* lives to live. We mature only by learning to face and resolve the matters that come our way.

Friends who are wise *strengthen* us in spirit by telling us what they know—then they step back and let us do what needs to be done. In this way, we become capable and strong. Our friends may take the lead if necessary…or take second place and support us…but if they're wise, they *always* let us bear some of the real load of work required to handle our own issues.

God is wise. The Hebrew-Christian tradition teaches that we were made to be active co-workers with God. Here then is how to *pray into action:*

- *Begin by handing the whole situation over to God.* Trust that every situation or dilemma has a purpose. Trust that God is involved in it…from the beginning…in the muddled middle of it…and that God will direct the outcome, whatever that may be. Decide now that you will not try to direct any part of this…but that you *will* look for the part you are to play.

- *Ask to be directed in word and action.* Think of yourself as an actor needing script and stage directions. We get in trouble when we try to take over the director's job or the roles other people are meant to fill. So…every morning, ask to be directed in what you need to say and do. Go about your business. (If you develop the habit of listening in quiet and solitude, you'll sharpen your interior ability to actively listen throughout even the most hectic day.)

  Expect that the part you are to play—what you are to say or do next—*will* come to you. Don't worry about *how* you'll know. You'll know.

- *Be ready to speak and act.* Say what needs to be said. Do what needs to be done. Beware of trying to bend situations to your will. Beware of trying to pry responses out of other people.

- *Step aside.* Having said your bit…having done your part…relax in between your "scenes." Let the director and the other actors go on with the show.

- *Live expectantly.* Never accept any unhappy situation as the final act, no matter how much you're tempted to slide back into depression or despair. Life's great drama is always an amazing story in progress.

Strategy #5: Be Flexible—(That Is, Forgiving)

One source of depression is an *inflexible spirit.* "Inflexibility" describes a spirit that will not let go of offenses. Earlier, we noted that the ancients thought of an unforgiving spirit as being "hard," "like a stone." If you think this isn't true, listen to yourself the next time you think or talk about someone who's hurt you. (Hmm… isn't that a punishing, hard-edged tone in your voice?)

The other way we become inflexible is by believing others must live by our standards. Some of us play the "moral heavy-weight." We develop a highly refined sense that we know what's right (and wrong!) for everyone around us. We're so sure of ourselves—and so concerned others will do it wrong—that we don't respect their need to develop personal standards themselves. Then the people in our lives ignore us, strain against us, and move away from us. That's when we become bitter, heavy, even brittle in spirit.

In either case—whether we're hurt and offended, or uncomfortable and rejecting—we become judgmental. *And get this. We may truly see* how others are "doing it all wrong." But the problem is, we don't have the power to turn back the clock, to make things the way they were. And we don't have the power to "right all wrongs" and bring about justice for every offense.

Being judgmental…or being unbending in holding on to offenses…makes our spirit become like stone. Unforgiving, we sink into depression. All our vitality is drained out of us.

What judgments are you holding on to, gripping like a blade cutting into your own flesh? Who do you need to forgive? Is it—

→ *a person*—a parent, a child, a spouse or former lover, a friend, a boss…for wronging you?

→ *God*—for allowing others to have something and withholding it from you, or for allowing a circumstance or event to pressure or hurt you?

→ *yourself*—for not being perfect, for not having boundless love, energy, or resources, or for not living up to your own standards or expectations?

A word to the wise—forgiveness can take time. It really can take awhile to loosen your tight grip on an offense and let it go. But there's no time like *right now* to begin.

You can begin by thinking about all the vitality you can turn to healthy and creative uses…the reserves of physical energy your body will be able to use for immunity boosting and repair…the good emotional energy that will flood in like a fresh new current, setting you free to love and enjoy life again…the strength of spirit that will make you more resilient as you encounter future challenges. Forgiving not only frees you from depression, it helps you literally reclaim your life.

Forgiveness comes by practicing these simple, but transforming, steps:

- ***Step away from your loss.*** *You* are not the thing that was taken from you or harmed. You are not your lost childhood. You are not your set-back career. You are not your home or your favorite pastime. You are not your altered appearance or marred health. You are not the person you're grieving for—and staying stuck in sadness or anger for them will not help either one of you.

  You are *you. Let go of the thing you're gripping so tightly—realize it also has* you *by the throat!* Be willing to discover who you are again, apart from the person or thing you've lost.

- ***Step into a new role.*** Sometimes it's hard to let go of the past, of hurts, of lost dreams, or ended relationships—out of fear. What will happen to the script we wrote for ourselves and those we love? How will our lives be if we let go of those wonderful scenes we hold on to in our heads?

  When it comes to forgiveness, as in prayer, we need to realize we are not the best scriptwriters of our own lives. The whole world and its future is not in our power. Today's emphasis is on goal-setting, determining your destiny, and planning to get everything we want out of life—but these concepts do our spirits a disservice. We wind up focusing entirely on our "missed," "stolen" lives, and never tune in to greater forces that are at work around us. Letting go of the life and script we had planned means allowing a power greater than we are to direct things...and it means step-ping into our role as the directed.

- *Step into peace.* When we or someone else we love has been hurt, we carry a special fear—who will honor and dignify our hurt and loss? Who will carry the torch of justice for us, our child, our friend, if we don't carry it?

Carrying the torch for justice...*without the anger and hurt that weighs down the spirit...* involves a greater interior balancing act than most of us can pull off. We usually let anger take over. We believe we need the energy of anger in order to stay resolved and keep fighting. Instead, we become brittle and reactive. Combative. We think we're being strong...but our one response to every-thing—anger, without a healthy outlet—is draining our vitality and defeating us.

We must realize that we are not in a position to right all wrongs. On the other hand, if we *are* given a chance to correct a wrong, we must realize that we're not likely to right a situation by acting out of destructive anger. We can let our anger become determination and seek creative ways to resolve and correct wrongs.

A final word to the wise—as we've seen, our spirit is the core of our being. Depression that is generated from our spirit can be like the waves created by a stone dropped in a pond. It's likely to "ripple out" to other aspects of our being, causing emotional, mental, and even physical distress.

For these reasons, depression that is seated in the spirit needs to be faced directly—but it also must be treated patiently, and given time. We did not sink into depression overnight. And new ways of opening ourselves to God, praying our way into action, or being flexible will take time to transform us.

But soon the new actions we take will also begin to have ripple effects. Slowly and gently at first...then with greater force...the new waves of vitality *will* make themselves felt. And with that comes a sense that can only be described as a steadying peace "which tran-scends all understanding." [1]

5

Eating "Better Mood Food"

I was feeling discouraged about things. So at lunch I gave in and went back to the buffet bar for more rolls and mashed potatoes. Starches are my downfall," says Toni. "No surprise—after that I was truly depressed."

Rich says, "The morning was going fine...until coffee break. Someone had left chocolate cake for everyone in the break room, and I had a piece. After that it was hard to focus, and I felt a little sleepy. By early afternoon I was fighting my way through waves of depression—thinking how my life and my career are as sluggish and stuck in a rut as I feel. I can't figure out how a good day went bad."

Sometimes we're acutely aware that foods affect our moods. At other times we miss the connection.

Depression and diet can go hand in hand. What we feel affects what we eat and how much we eat. What we eat affects our biochemistry and alters our mood.

The great news is that our eating habits can become allies instead of enemies as we learn to reverse the depression spiral.

Depressing Diets

Food can have a powerful effect on our moods. Strangely enough, most of us are largely unaware of how *great* an effect it does have. Getting out of the depression spiral can require us to become more focused on our eating and its effects.

For instance, some of us experience mood swings because of the *amount* we eat. Most of us eat far more than our energy needs require. We overload our system, resulting in sluggishness and sleepiness. Over time we lose interest in sustained physical work or exercise and feel generally fatigued. Then comes the weight gain and we "just don't feel that good." Now we feel down about ourselves…and just plain down.

There are variations on this theme, of course. We may not overeat *all* the time. But too often we stuff ourselves or cram our food in too quickly…once again overloading ourselves and forcing our body's biochemistry into overdrive to handle the job of digesting the mass.

Then, of course, some of us experience mood swings because of *what* we eat.

It's no secret that the Western diet is high in sugar, fat, and salt. No secret that we love our breads, pastries, chips, and cookies. Our sizzling quarter-pound burgers and soft drinks sold at quick-stops in pail-sized "cups." Even if we're not in the rapidly growing category of Westerners now classed as "obese," our diet is likely to be quite a bit off the mark from the healthy, energy-producing, mood-lifting diet we should be eating.

And then there are others of us whose depressions are caused at least in part by the limited or severely restrictive diets we eat.

We're not just talking here to the high-fashion models who exist on celery and bottled water. We're addressing those who—

- live on pizza, or beef, or cereal, or follow any other diet focused around one, two, or three foods
- live on a restricted diet for bodybuilding purposes
- live on almost nothing due to an eating disorder like anorexia, bulimia, or body dysmorphia (distorted body image)

When we severely restrict our eating, we disrupt our body's normal biochemistry and normal brain function. This can be one reason why people who are overthin because of an eating disorder still see themselves as "fat"—and also why bodybuilders who are hugely muscled and "ripped" see themselves as "too small." It may not be just mental conditioning—the result of comparing themselves to others. Instead, the brain is functioning in a way that allows them to misperceive reality. Truly, they are operating with an "altered consciousness"…and too often with severely altered and depressive moods.

If you are, or suspect you are, dealing with an eating disorder such as anorexia or bulimia or with body dysmorphia…contact a physician, a psychiatrist, or a psychologist as soon as possible. These conditions are serious. They can result in permanent damage to your heart and other internal organs, and they can be life-threatening.

Today—right now—make a commitment to find help. You do not need to live with the anxiety, depression, fatigue, and poor health these conditions bring. With good support, you can turn these conditions around…and find mental and emotional relief.

Mindless Eating

In each type of poor dietary habit lies one more basic habit—a sort of mindless unconsciousness about food…and a poor relationship to our personal energy needs and moods. As a result, what we need to eat isn't even close to what we feed on.

We can turn the habit of mindless eating around. To do so, we only need to get ahold of some simple strategies for better eating. Where low mood is related to food, we can make strides up and out of depression by focusing on:

- *the conditions surrounding our eating*—such as emotional factors that drive our eating

- *the effects various kinds of food have on us*

- *eliminating or minimizing foods that create mood chaos…* sending us down…or up, then down

- *focusing on foods that keep us physically energized and our moods level*

Try the following simple and healthful strategies to help you hit these better-eating goals.

EAT BETTER…*FEEL* BETTER

Strategy #1: Eat "Mindfully"

"Mindful eating" doesn't mean condemning ourselves to a search for the "Himalayan Mystic's Whole Grain and Yak Broth Diet for Achieving Alternate Consciousness." It means focusing our approach to eating so that we're eating for health and well-being.

Mindful eating can help us—

- understand our own pattern of energy and mood highs and lows
- discover what triggers mindless and "escape" eating
- detect the foods that plunge us into a slump, and which ones juice us up with a temporary high...and then send us crashing down
- empower ourselves with the knowledge of which foods carry us on a more constant and level cushion of good mood and constant energy

Here is one helpful way to develop mindful eating:

1. *Choose a target week.* For seven days focus on how your moods affect your eating habits, and how eating various foods affects you.

2. *Create a "Food-Mood Notebook."* Keep a notebook at hand. Devote a page to each day. Divide each page into fourths. Allow one quarter-page for each meal. In each of the first three quarters of a page, write (down the left side):

I Ate: (to catalog everything you ate at a given meal, and any snacks)

I Did: (to note any events that occurred around the time of your eating)

I Felt: (to capture your mood and physical reactions during and between meals)

I See: (to observe the interplay between food, events, and your moods)

On the final quarter-page, write, on the left:

Changes: (to activate new healthy habits and help let go of old unhealthy ones)

3. **Focus in.** To explain how this can work for you, let's look at a sample page from a notebook in progress. Watch how mood and food can affect you in a given day.

FOOD-MOOD JOURNAL SAMPLE

I Ate: *Breakfast:* Orange juice; egg substitute scrambled with peppers, olives, and chunked ham; a banana. *Snack*: Cottage cheese with pineapple.

I Did: Worked steadily all morning on reports at the computer. Interrupted by a call from impatient client—a bit accusing. Defused his anger with reassurances.

I Felt: Alert and pretty energetic all morning…until phone call made me frustrated. (One big client is never grateful for extra work—but complains loudly about tiniest delays.)

I See: When I eat a healthy breakfast and mid-morning snack, my energy level remains even.

I Ate: *Lunch:* Three packs of cheese-and-peanut-butter crackers. Cola. *Snack:* Two small bags of corn chips. Diet cola. *Other:* Three cups of coffee w/ cream & sugar. Candy bar.

I Did: Worked through lunch break and till about 3:00 (getting ahead to keep the client "happy"—if that's possible). At 3:00 creativity died. Wasted time on gabby phone calls and shuffling papers.

I Felt: Suddenly drowsy about 2:00 P.M. Then wired on coffee. End of the afternoon, feeling bloated and stomach is "off"—also irritated and unhappy about work.

I See: Eating junk food wrecked the steady energy flow I had going. Also made my stomach feel gross. Coffee made me sweaty and tense.

I Ate: *Dinner:* Pot roast, mashed potatoes, corn, two rolls, small salad, apple pie. *Other:* Two glasses of red wine at bedtime.

I Did: Sat in front of TV all evening (only intended to watch the news).

I Felt: Worn out. Overfull. Like I'd "blown it" with the healthy eating already—so pigged-out at dinner. Felt even more like my life is out of control and stuck. Couldn't focus when son wanted to talk, so I felt more useless. By bedtime, just felt sad and sorry for myself. Wanted to numb out a little.

I See: Eating a heavy evening meal didn't give me energy, it weighed me down more. TV marathons contribute to my "going no place fast" feeling. Numbing myself to sleep with wine when I'm feeling down is a habit I don't like.

Changes: I need to make healthy eating a priority again tomorrow. Need to keep anger about clients from making me take my focus off good habits so that I give in to bad work, eating, and emotional habits. Instead, I'll take a "health break" and stretch or walk for 10 minutes. Also pack more fruit for snacks.

Important Variations: You may also wish to use the "Food-Mood Journal" to track the effects of such specific mood-altering foods as sugar or simple carbohydrates like bread and grains. Or you may want to use it in an elimination diet if you suspect you're having an allergic or other bad reaction to a certain food. In that case, remember to eliminate *only one food at a time.*

Strategy #2: Lean on the White Meats

The digestion of red meat requires our bodies to put out a lot of energy. Most people hit a physical lull and feel mentally fuzzy after a main course of the red stuff. Yes, we are omnivores, but it seems we need to consume very, very little red meat—despite what our taste buds may tell us.

We don't have to cut red meats out of our diet entirely. But we can help ourselves maintain a better mood by rebalancing our diet so that we're eating more white meat.

What's so good about white meats?

White meats tend to be naturally higher in the essential fatty acids (EFAs) omega-3 (alpha-linolenic acid) and omega-6 (gamma-linoleic acid). Some stores carry white-meat cuts from animals that were specially fed to ensure higher natural levels of the EFAs, and to ensure that the meat has a balance of both omega-3 and -6 fatty acids.

While we're on EFAs—you need to know that they are vitally important in powering and regulating many body functions—including circulation, immunity, reproduction, breathing, and digestion. Proper levels of EFAs also help us achieve a biochemical balance that assists in maintaining a level mood. Besides that, digesting white meat doesn't drain the body's energy the way digesting red meat does.

When stocking your fridge and freezer with white meats, buy:

Chicken. Check the brands. Some producers inject their poultry with fluids to pump up the water weight. Many people who are conscientious about their health have switched to eating free-range chicken raised on grain containing DHA (one of the omega-3 fatty acids), which makes the meat high in EFAs.

Fish. Many studies have shown that cultures that eat fish as a main meat source have about *one-tenth* of the depression of cultures that don't eat fish. Leaving aside other cultural differences, this may be due in part to the fact that fish are high in…essential fatty acids. And of course, the meat of fish contains many other important nutrients—like vitamins B-6, B-12, and folic acid.

Especially recommended for your grocery cart are the following fish (and other seafoods). Those containing the most EFAs are listed at the top:

> ><> anchovies, herring, mackerel, salmon
>
> ><> albacore tuna, sablefish, sardines
>
> ><> bluefin tuna, trout
>
> ><> halibut, swordfish
>
> ><> freshwater bass, oysters
>
> ><> sea bass
>
> ><> pollock, shrimp
>
> ><> catfish, crabs
>
> ><> clams, cod, flounder, scallops

Turkey. Turkey is high in tryptophan, a natural amino acid needed for the brain's production of neurotransmitting chemicals. Current research indicates that when these chemicals are low because they're being reabsorbed into the brain tissue too quickly, the result is anxiety or depression or both.

After you leave your grocer's meat cases and head through the dairy aisle, throw in:

Eggs. Free-range chicken eggs are what you want. Because they come from those chickens raised on special feed, these eggs will be balanced in omega-6 and omega-3 fatty acids.

FOUR BIG "IFS"
～

If you love red meats… learn to know which cuts are the lowest in fat.

If your recipe calls for "ground"…remember that most grocery stores now rate ground red meats by the percentage of fat they contain, down to about 7 percent. Also consider that a mix of ground beef and ground turkey gives you the red-meat flavor with less fat in your burgers, chili, and tacos.

If you fry it…you're trapping in fat and chemical pollutants that need to run off during cooking—and you're also adding the fat of the frying oil. But….

If you bake, broil, or grill…in a pan that separates the meat from the drippings, you are losing unneeded fat and many toxins.

Strategy #3: Heavy on the Veggies

Diets low in the complex carbohydrates can contribute to the depletion of serotonin in your brain and therefore to depressive states. What's needed is a diet rich in raw or steamed vegetables. As your mom said, "Eat your vegetables!"

*But…*all vegetables aren't created equal. Some are more beneficial for people who are dealing with mood dips and the low energy associated with depression.

Most especially, stock up on:

Dark green leafy vegetables. These nutritional powerhouses contain high amounts of the B-vitamins and trace minerals that are rapidly depleted in our system when depression and emotional distress go to work on us. Include in your grocery cart:

• collards	• kombu	• hijiki
• nori	• kale	• spinach

Energy-rich vegetables. Those most frequently recommended for their energy/mood-boosting nutrients include:

- artichokes
- sprouts
- asparagus
- cauliflower
- broccoli
- mushrooms
- brussels sprouts
- carrots (especially raw)
- turnips

Soybeans, Tofu. Soybeans and their derivative products provide another great source of complex carbohydrates for boosting serotonin. Not only that, they're a healthful source of protein—very important for those who need to eat a diet low in red meats.

Strategy #4: "Big" on Fruits

Some mood- and energy-boosting diets recommend consuming "plenty of carbohydrates"—and suggest foods from the starchy, simple-carbohydrate categories like breads, pastas, and grains.

Unfortunately, starchy carbohydrates increase the body's production of insulin. Many of us are genetically predisposed to insulin resistance, or we become insulin-resistant as we age. This means that food energy carried in the bloodstream to the cells is not used efficiently by our cells. As a result the food energy is wasted and eliminated...or packed onto our bodies as fat. And as you may guess, starchy carbohydrates that promote greater insulin production create a greater problem for diabetics.

For this reason, even though breads, grains, and pastas are suggested in some diets, they are recommended here with caution: *Learn to eat these things in smaller servings.*

Overall, plan to eat these complex-carbohydrate fruits:

- apples
- mangoes
- avocados
- pears
- cherries
- pineapples
- blueberries
- strawberries

Vary your fruit intake, both to keep yourself from getting bored and so that you'll get important nutrients that vary from fruit to fruit—such as potassium, magnesium, and zinc. Besides the healthy dose of carbohydrates, fruits will give you high amounts of vitamin C (which is also necessary for energy production) and fiber.

Strategy #5: "Good" fat

Some fats are bad and contribute to overall poor health. That includes animal fats and the monounsaturated fats in cottonseed,

DRINK THE "CLEAR STUFF"

∾

When we're dehydrated we put an extra load on every system of our body. Electrolyte levels fall, and metabolisms slow. We feel generally depleted, and our mood goes "down."

Some sources of dehydration are obvious—like overexertion at work or play, and sickness. Some sources are not so obvious, but are all too common—like coffee and tea consumption, winter heating and summer air-conditioning, and sudden changes from cool or mild weather to warm or hot weather, even for a day or two. To counter dehydration and its mood-crippling effects:

Avoid caffeinated drinks. Sure, they give you a temporary boost. But they also encourage dependence on that "false" boost. And these drinks act to flush fluid *out* of your system.

Drink refreshing water throughout the day. Okay, you've heard the recommendation: Drink eight 8-ounce glasses of water every day. Sounds like a great way to kill your day hunting for a restroom, doesn't it? If you try to achieve this goal all at once, that's exactly how it will be. But here's an alternative:

⚘ Build up your water intake slowly by keeping a glass (or bottle) of fresh, cool water at hand. By sipping a little at a time, every so often, you'll eventually be taking in a healthful amount every day…and you'll allow your body time to build up to the extra fluid slowly. Believe it or not, you *won't* be crossing your legs in meetings or in the car, because your body will adjust. And your blood, tissues, and organs will be getting a healthy "flush" from toxins.

⚘ Drink cool water, which won't shock and stress your system, like ice water.

"Drink green." Green tea is a wonderful switcheroo from coffee. You'll still get the hot, pleasant drink. You'll get *off* the peaks-and-drops ride of caffeine drinks. And you'll be taking in high doses of antioxidants, an added benefit.

soybean, and tropical oils—like that artery-choking dietary horror they pour over theater popcorn.

Other fats actually contribute to better health and even mood-lifting. Olive oil is highly recommended for healthy eating, though it doesn't contribute to a mood-lifting diet. Fats that are beneficial for us, because they contain those important EFAs, come in:

- canola oil
- flax seeds
- chia seeds
- hemp oil
- flaxseed oil
- perilla oil

CHOCOLATE

Chocolate—in a book on health and wellness? But chocolate is loaded with sugar and fat and….

First justification: You can't be good all the time. And a *little* chocolate, with its richness and "chew-satisfaction," is a rich reward for being good.

Second justification (the health-benefit one): The cocoa beans that give us chocolate are high in chemicals that increase the brain's production of endorphins and serotonin—chemicals that relieve pain and lift the mood.

Yes, taken in big doses, the fat and sugar in chocolate will quickly elevate your blood sugar…which will then quickly drop and send you spinning into a mood and energy crash. So…

Eat just an ounce—a piece about the size of a walnut—at a time. And enjoy chocolate's benefits without the crash. And remember that dark chocolate has less sugar and fat than milk chocolate—and white chocolate has no health benefits at all.

Strategy #6: Eat "in Balance" for Mood Balance

We are omnivores. We need to eat like omnivores. This means eating the *right balance* of proteins, carbohydrates, and fats. (Notice that the previous sentence says "the *right balance*" of these necessary nutrients.) Many of us eat in *unbalanced* ways that pretty much guarantee we're stressing our bodies and crashing our own moods.

"All-Protein Pete" is toxifying his kidneys. "Sue, the Obsessively Thin Salad-Bar Grazer," never gives her body the tiny and all-important dose of healthy fat needed to metabolize food well (not to mention the rest of what's missing from her diet). If you're "Bob, the Sugar-and-Carb King," and your lunch is a pack of cupcakes and a cola, and your supper is a pizza, here's a word of advice: *Set aside money now in a high-return investment fund for all the health-care bills you're going to have later.*

Besides eating the right foods…some of which are listed in the "Strategies" above…learn to eat meals with a good balance of healthy proteins, carbohydrates, and fats.

Here's what we need in our meals to keep our mood and energy levels balanced:

- *protein—30 percent of calories*
- *carbohydrates—40 percent of calories*
- *fats—30 percent of calories* [2]

Practice these important mood-lifting diet suggestions:

1. *Eat smaller meals.* This is a healthy practice, because over-loading your digestive tract unnecessarily drains energy. Learn to push back from the table even before your brain registers "full." Your brain will register full a few minutes after you really *are* full. So if you're still pushing it in when your "full" light comes on, it's too late. You've overeaten.

2. *Answer* between-meal "*hunger calls*" *with healthy snack items* like fruit or commercial snack bars that offer the balance of nutri-ents described above. We are not out to starve ourselves by stinting on meals, then ignoring hunger signals.

Strategy #7: When you stray from the "straight-and-narrow" of better eating…return quickly

In the New Testament parable of the "prodigal son," the kid blew it big-time…and wound up eating pig food. Still, he had the good sense to realize there is no future in a bad diet. He quickly trucked his way back home, both to clean up his act *and* his eating.

Sometimes, even with the best of intentions, we stray from the dietary straight-and-narrow. Depression tends to exaggerate every failure, including our dietary lapses. Hopeless thinking engulfs the way we see ourselves. One ice-cream binge and we start to believe we're trapped in the depressive-diet zone forever.

If you feel *like you've blown it by overeating or eating grossly out of balance…*don't compound it by telling yourself, "I blew it, so I might as well quit trying to eat in balance."

*Remember, the fact is…*you are always only one meal away from eating healthily and in balance again. String together your successes, not your failures, and you will stay on track better until you form a new habit of eating for health and mood-lifting.

Use these techniques to help stay on the better-diet track:

- *Adapt your "Food-Mood Journal" and make it a "planner."* Use it to help you keep your mood stable by

    — *anticipating stressful and potentially "down" days*

    — *planning healthy meals and snacks in advance*

    — *planning mood-lifting breaks where possible*

    — *planning for a "day after" if you've had a "down" day, to allow yourself to regain your emotional footing and better eating habits if necessary.*

- *Fire your "inner critic."* Remember, in sports it's "the opposing side" that offers jeers and catcalls when you fail to score. They *want* you to fail. Every one of us has an "inner critic"—and in depressed people the voice that reminds us we're not making it is loud. Identify that voice every time it speaks to condemn you when your eating isn't the best…*and "fire" the critic.*

- *Hire an "inner coach."* Adopt the voice of a *coach.* A coach is someone who helps us achieve our greatest potential and get to the win. A coach will notice when we've made mistakes…but will then offer instruction to correct. *Let your "coach's" voice be the one that* encourages you to eat better.

- *Allow yourself "treat" days.* What's your treat? Make a place for it in your life. Maybe Friday evening when you go out for some fun. Or Saturday or Sunday, going to a movie or a sporting event.

Serious deprivation usually doesn't work—unless total abstinence from some food is crucial for health reasons…or unless you know you are better off going cold turkey than trying to dabble.

Solomon's proverb, *"Do not be over-righteous…Do not be over-wicked"*[3] was surely meant for those of us who are eating to achieve balance in our lives!

SNACK COUNTERATTACK

∼

If sugary, fatty snack-attacks are a big downfall for you, sending you into the dumps…plan to counterattack. Here are the "rules of war":

Keep nutritious, good-tasting snacks on hand. Don't be caught off guard by genuine hunger…or by the tempting scent of french fries wafting from Greasy-Burger Bistro.

At home, your arsenal can include:

—bagels   —sorbet   —yogurt   —Cheerios
—low-fat, low-salt microwave popcorn
—carrot sticks (with 1 TBSP low-fat dressing for dip)

On the road, don't count on every convenience store to have healthful snacks. Take-alongs that won't wreak havoc with your mood include:

— dried fruit   —low-fat fig bars
—apples, orange slices, pears   — low-salt pretzels

6

Boosting Your Body

Depression is a state we most often associate with our mind. The word *depression* calls to mind sad or negative thinking, or "feeling empty or down." Or we think of depression as based in the emotions or spirit, and recall times when our soul felt "trapped," "heavy," or "hopeless."

With all this emphasis on *mind* and *mood*, we often overlook the fact that some causes of depression can actually be physiological—resulting from biochemical changes—and also from problems that have settled, so to speak, into our very joints, blood, and muscles. Often, before we even know what's happening to us, these physical changes and problems send us down the chute emotionally.

The good news is that we can do something to counteract what we might call "body-based" causes of depression.

The Body Has "a Mind of Its Own"

What are the *body-based* causes of depression? Some include:

→ vitamin and mineral deficiencies

→ chronic pain from injury or disease

→ "hidden" illness—one that's in its early or onset stage, as yet undetected

The body, so to speak, has a mind or voice of its own. Sometimes depression happens when our body is trying to tell us something is out of balance and we're not ready or willing to listen.

81

Understand this: *Pain or sickness can be major contributors to depression—even sickness of which we're only "pre-conscious." If you suspect that your depression may be linked to one of these causes, you should see your physician immediately for a complete physical checkup.* (Scheduling a regular physical, especially once we hit 40, is a great idea in any case!)

Other causes of body-based depression include—

→ sedentary work or an inactive lifestyle or both

→ lack of sleep or poor quality of sleep

→ physically impairing habits such as high alcohol, drug, or nicotine intake

→ taxing the body by overwork—including strenuous and too-frequent weight lifting and aerobic workouts

Life habits like these work to weaken or "depress" us physiologically, leaving us with

• low muscle tone

• sluggish metabolism

• poorly oxygenated blood

• stressed muscles, joints, and cardiovascular system, and possible stress fractures of the bones

Overwork or underwork *both* create the conditions that contribute to body-based depression. Underworking is more common for most of us, by far.

"Hold on a Minute…!"

You may be thinking, *That's not fair to say I underwork. I work at a stressful job five [or more] days a week. I'm pretty beat when I come home. Then I still have to face work around the house—in the yard, in the home office…plus commitments to my family, community, or church. I'm wiped out at the end of a day!*

Yes, a lot of the work we do *at* work—including mental work—*is* taxing. But it rarely leaves us with a "good fatigue." Short bursts of "weekend-warrior" work around the house and yard don't give it to us either. Most often, we're left at the end of a day with pent-up energy stored in the large-muscle groups of the body. We're left with a fatigue that can be described as "mentally tired but restless." And at bedtime we fall into a kind of sleep that isn't very deep or refreshing. Next morning, we feel a bit depleted, slow, and sluggish…maybe cranky…and we probably rely on a caffeine jolt to get ourselves "up and moving." Without making the connection as to how our mood has slipped we're soon thinking, *Life is pretty dull and boring,* or *Life is really disappointing.*

This scenario describes someone whose living habits are creating the conditions for body-based depression. We often have no clue that our physical lethargy has contributed to our dullness of mind and spirit or to our less-than-optimum physical well-being.

Needed—A Commitment to…Your Body

We need to recognize that physical fitness can be one important key to mental, emotional, and spiritual wellness. To maintain fitness we need a simple, workable regimen that will give our muscles a good workout and increase our cardiovascular and aerobic output at the same time.

To be clear—this isn't a challenge to get "buff" or "ripped" like those muscle-magazine models who have dehydrated themselves with diuretics and laxatives in order to look "great" for the 8-hour photo shoot, or the fashion models who are 20-percent collagen and high-tech plastics. This doesn't mean becoming a "gym bum."

What we need is a commitment to personal physical wellness—a commitment to *work for the benefit of our bodies.* This means:

- **making personal physical fitness a primary goal,** so we can help our bodies function at their best by
- **creating a physical workout plan** that fits with our other life commitments, and
- **changing our workout plan…**so it doesn't become boring but continues to keep us "on the edge" of challenge

Studies on the relationship between depression and physical workout—including all types of workouts—reveal this: If your output of physical energy is low, you are *twice* as likely to slump into depression as someone who gets modest exercise (say, occasional walking, jogging, or easy bike-riding). And you are three times more likely to become depressed than someone who exercises more intensely (aerobics, dancing, serious cycling, weight lifting).

Fortunately, when depression has worked itself *into* our physical bodies, we have many solutions at our disposal—choices suited to every taste—so we can work it *out*.

Here are some strategies that will help you break out of body-based depression, beginning with the simplest.

WORKING OUT DEPRESSION
Strategy #1: Take One Step (Take Any Step)

One of the characteristics of depression is that we become stuck...unable to take steps in a new direction.

Sometimes we don't even see that we're stuck because we may be functioning at a reasonable, even a high, level in some aspect of life. Maybe we're able to perform our job well but just can't begin to get it together to check out the costs of a health club membership. Or maybe we can keep up with household tasks—but feel overwhelmed at committing to a workout schedule...or at even getting out the door to the gym.

The last thing you may need right now is the challenge of setting up some big-time workout regimen. You can still benefit greatly by taking *just one simple step.*

What good does taking the first step do? By *not* committing to some big challenge, we're relieved of the pressure of potential failure. Now we're free to do *just* the simple thing, and we seem to loosen up inside. We take the little step, knowing it's "enough," and we see our competency in small-frame. We've taken control of one small portion of our world. Tomorrow we can take another step. Today we've been in motion!

Does taking the small step sound good? Then do this: Begin by exploring types of exercise that best suit you. Also consider when you'll fit a workout into your day. There are several ways to do this:

- Purchase a health or exercise magazine—one that seems suited to your age and workout ability
- Borrow an exercise book or video from your local library
- Stop by a fitness center and ask for a tour so you can check out the equipment and exercise programs they offer

You may also want to:

- Take a look at your weekly schedule to determine when you could fit in three 30-minute workouts. If possible, plan them at the same time on each of those days.

- Consider simple goals—like targeting a start-up date or picking up inexpensive cotton sweats and t-shirts and suitable shoes. *Avoid* making big, long-term goals right away— like "I'm going to exercise every other day for a whole year" or "...until I lose 20 [30, 40] pounds."

The whole point is, *Hit some simple, easy marks first.* There's a term for the important step you're taking if you do any one of these things—it's called "getting your head in the game."

Okay. But is this simple act of forming good intentions *enough*? Didn't someone once come up with the saying "The road to hell is paved with good intentions"? In response to that poor cynical soul I say, *"So is the road to success."*

For greater benefit

- Find someone willing to act as your "coach" or "encourager"— someone who will help you get started and check in with you regularly to help you abide by those good intentions.

- Find yourself a "workout buddy." You can keep each other on track on those days when one of you would rather give in to depression (or stay at home eating a donut).

Strategy #2: Give Yourself the Gift of Oxygen

Proper breathing, in combination with stretching, is an anyone-can-do-it workout that yields more benefits to the body than we might imagine. When we make this simple workout part of our day, we give our bodies the useful "gift" of much-needed oxygen *and* help move toxins out of our system much more quickly.

Normally, most of us breathe shallowly, using just the chest muscles to inhale. We fill only the top part of our lungs with air. This means we take in less oxygen, which is needed to help with all organ and tissue functions, and we also allow much of the toxic carbon dioxide our body needs to expel to remain in our lungs.

Proper breathing is what we need—that is, deep and slow breathing. We do this by bringing the large diaphragm muscle below the ribs into play. This muscle turns the lungs into bellows, and normally works only when our body is exerting itself and more oxygen is needed faster. Breathing with the diaphragm expels the toxic gases collected in our lungs and gives our bodies the generous treat of well-oxygenated blood.

Stretching is the other half of this simple gift to our bodies. The slow, deliberate *flexing* and *extension* of our body's large muscle-groups—

- increases cardiovascular functioning and blood flow
- increases the delivery of oxygen and nutrients to the cells and tissues
- forces toxins out of cells and tissues for quicker elimination from our body

Do this for proper breathing:

1. Sit comfortably in a chair with your feet flat on the floor. Keep your back straight but not rigid, and your head up.

2. Inhale slowly and gently through your nose. Use your diaphragm to expand your chest fully. Exhale through your mouth. Concentrate as you do this—the goal is to keep up the pattern indefinitely without becoming light-headed from hyperventilating.

Do this for "start-up" stretching:

1. For your *upper body*:

- Hold your arms straight out in front of you, with palms together "prayer style." Raise your arms slowly till your fingertips are pointing at the ceiling. Stretch up…hold. Arch your back (but don't strain)…hold. Return slowly to the original position. *Relax.* Repeat as you like. (You're remembering to breathe properly, aren't you?)

- Repeat the above stretch…but begin with your palms open and facing down. Raise your arms slowly toward the ceiling "surrender style." Stretch…spread your arms slowly…and bring them down to your sides. *Relax.* (Repeat.)

- With your arms in front of you, form a circle, as if you are hugging someone, and clasp your hands. Raise them just above head height—but not straight over your head. With your left arm, slowly pull your right arm across and down...until you feel your right shoulder muscles and the muscles down the right side of your back stretching. (Do not move your torso.) Repeat for the opposite side. Return to center. *Relax.*

2. For your *mid-section:*

    *   Put your arms in front of you again in a circle, hands clasped. Keep them level, and with the right arm, slowly pull the left arm as far right as it will go...about even with your right shoulder. Allow your torso to turn—but not your hips—until you feel your abdominals stretching. Repeat to benefit the opposite side. Return to center. *Relax.*

3. For your *legs* and *buttocks:*

    *   Still seated, keep one foot flat on the floor. Extend your other leg so just the heel is resting on the floor. Clasp your hands behind your back. Gently lower your torso toward your out-stretched left leg. *Do not force yourself forward or "bounce," as this can cause injuries.* Feel the stretch in your calf, back, and back of the thigh. Repeat for the opposite side. *Relax.*

    *   Seated, cross your left leg, so your left ankle bone rests on your right knee. Again, clasp your hands behind your back. Gently lower your torso toward your right knee...as if you are going to touch your forehead to your ankle bone. *Do not force.* Feel the stretch in your left hip and buttocks.

You can easily create your own routine using these stretches and others for the back and neck.

A note about necks: Never roll your head to loosen and stretch neck muscles. Doing so can damage the delicate disks between the vertebrae. Instead, gently tilt the head forward and back...then side to side...using your fingertips to work out tight muscles.

The physical aspects of exercises such as yoga and tai chi have value apart from the religious philosphies that are sometimes taught with them. It's easy to find instructors, videos, and books that focus on the exercises, which will give you the workout you need.

LIGHTEN UP
～

The human body craves sunlight. If we don't get enough, the brain will produce too-small quantities of key hormones. The lowering of these hormone levels results in depression. This is why those of us in the colder climes tend to feel down during the dark winter months…and why some of us even suffer from serious bouts of winter-season depression known as Seasonal Affective Disorder (SAD).

One good solution is to purchase a full-spectrum light box, available in pet stores, health food stores, and some discount stores. The light this kind of equipment puts out is very close to natural light.

A great solution is to get ourselves out for a brisk walk every day. A half-hour walk is good. An hour would be great. Besides giving our heart and lungs a workout, we'll get the light we need to "lighten up" our mood.

Strategy #3: Simple Massage

In some cultures, massage is considered part of a good health regimen. Here in the West, we are just discovering its benefits to physical health.

Do this if you're interested in simple massage: Contact a local LMT (Licensed Massage Therapist) and enjoy the healthful relaxation he or she provides. Or you can obtain an illustrated book on massage and get your partner to trade personal massages with you.

If you visit an LMT, if you're like most people, at first you may feel uneasy being touched by a stranger. Give yourself time to get over it. Most important, you'll be amazed at how great it feels to relax under the care of an expert at massage.

Recommended Reading: Massage for Dummies: *A Reference for the Rest of Us* by Steve Capellini and Michel Van Welden (Indianapolis: Hungry Minds, Inc., 1999).

Strategy #4: Walk It Off

A mild injury in school sports, or frustration on the field, always brought the same advice from our coach: *"Walk it off."*

When we need to work depression out of the physical body, "walk it off" is still good advice. Walking at a *moderate* to *vigorous* pace is a great way to literally move yourself out of depression.

Do this for a fantastic walk:

1. *Work out two or three routes.* Try to pick one short (10-minutes) one mid-range (20-minutes), and one long course (30-minutes or more). This will offer you changes of scenery and options to choose from depending on how much time you have to walk on a given day.

2. *Invest in good walking shoes.* This means shoes that can "breathe" and that support your foot and ankle well. The $15 discount-house "cheapies" are…well…*cheap.* Your feet and legs deserve better.

3. *When you set out…leave your cares behind.* It may help to have a small mental or even actual ritual to help you do this:

- Tell yourself, "All negative thinking stops when I close the door behind me."

- Take your jacket off the hook and temporarily "hang up your troubles" in its place.

4. *Get your* walking rhythm *and your* pulse *up.* You'll want to achieve a rhythm in your stride that is aggressive enough to encourage proper deep breathing and that you can sustain through most of your walk. You can easily check your pulse by placing the index and middle finger of your left hand on your right medial artery—that blue "pencil" line at the base of the left thumb.

FYI—here are target heart-rates that you can shoot for if you want the best aerobic workout during your walk (or any other exercise). Achieving your target rate for at least 30 minutes, three times a week, is a very good thing to do.

TARGET HEART-RATE RANGE

Age	Range
25	117 to 156 beats per minute (20 to 26 beats per 10 seconds)
35	111 to 148 beats per minute (19 to 25 beats per 10 seconds)
45	105 to 140 beats per minute (18 to 23 beats per 10 seconds)
55	99 to 132 beats per minute (17 to 22 beats per 10 seconds)
65+	93 to 124 beats per minute (16 to 21 beats per 10 seconds)

5. *Let your mind relax* once you've established your rhythm and gotten your pulse-rate up. Walking while emptying your head and fixing on some new blue horizon is a great way to encourage a healthy perspective.

Or you may prefer to *pray*...unburdening your soul to God. Others may like to set out with a *positive affirmation* circulating in the spirit—good "soul food" to chew on along the way.

6. *Slow your pace* as your walk comes to an end. Give yourself a good 10- to 15-minute cooldown period. *It's never a good idea, after elevating your heart-rate, to sit or lie down immediately. Let your body adjust to a "quiet" level of activity.*

For greater benefit: During a long walk insights often come to us; and problems seem to "solve themselves," while the fretting, anxious mind is out of gear and the spirit is opened by prayer. Start a journal to capture the insights and ideas for life changes that come to you...as a step toward *acting on them.*

Strategy #5: Work It Out...Play to Sweat...Shake It Up

When it comes to mood-lifting activities, nothing beats working or playing yourself into a good sweat.

Clearly, playing cards, chess, or the newest "Battle Zoids" video game does not count as physical activity. What *does count* is healthy athletic activity that raises your heart rate for at least 30 minutes. This has amazing benefits because it boosts the production of the brain's neurotransmitting chemicals that affect our mood. (For those overachievers among us: Working out intensely for *more* than one hour has fewer benefits than a 30-minute workout, and it can actually be harmful.)

Depending on the type of activity you choose, you can also experience social benefits that are mood-lifting.

A caution: If you experience chronic pain due to muscle, joint, or spinal injury, do not push yourself through any kind of strenuous workout. In this case pain is *not* gain. You cannot "get over" a muscle or joint injury by "pushing through" it.

Also: If you have other health conditions, especially those affecting the heart, lungs, or vascular system, have yourself checked out by a physician *before* starting any physically intense regimen.

Do this for a great workout:

Check out local teams put together by church and community leagues. Being part of a team brings you into contact with humor, reality, sadness, joy, trickery, struggle *and* victory in other people's lives. If you make it your goal to know something about the lives of the people you play with it can open up your perspective and be a far more rewarding experience. Line, country, and ballroom dancing can also have similar benefits.

If you prefer more of a personal challenge, sign up for lessons and get into tennis, racquetball, tae kwan do, karate, boxing, or non-impact aerobics (see Strategy #7).

If you want to build even greater physical strength and endurance:

- Join a health club or gym where you can work out under the guidance of a trainer who can show you how to do it the right way.
- Join a cycling, hiking, or climbing club—again, supervised by people who know the sport.

Strategy #6: Good Sex

In case you're wondering, this suggested strategy is not a joke. Sexual intercourse has the physical benefit of increasing the production of serotonin in the brain, which creates a powerful mood lift. But more important than that, the emotional intimacy and honesty required to keep a healthy sexual relationship growing is a very healthy and important preventative for depression.

Do this for healthy sexual intimacy:

1. Make a commitment to exploring all the ramifications of the word *intimacy*. It means honesty. Learning to ask for what you need. Learning to ask what someone else needs. Anything and everything we learn about intimacy with our partner is useful for every part of life…not just the sexual relationship.

2. If you or your partner has problems or depression related to sexual issues…*make an appointment today* to see a counselor who can help you work through these issues. Even if you have to overcome some hesitancy or embarrassment, doing this can change your life and possibly heal a dying relationship.

For the greatest benefits: Intercourse and sexual intimacy are God-given gifts that enhance committed, monogamous relationships. Too many of us make the mistake of believing life would be better and our intimate needs more fulfilled if we had a new partner (they won't be) or if the partner we have could only read our minds (they can't) and give us what only we know we need.

- Make a commitment to deepen or renew your relationship by being the one to bravely take it to a new level of intimacy.

- Share a secret about yourself—any secret your partner may not know about you. Something as simple as an old memory you haven't brought up before…or as risky as a desire you'd like to fulfill in bed. Make sure they know in advance this is important to you, how risky this is for you to share (1 being a little, 10 being a lot). Also make sure they know you're asking for their understanding and support.

- Hold on to this attitude: *Truly intimate relationships are too great, and sexual love is too wonderful a gift, to let either become a casualty of depression.*

Strategy #7: Get "Loose" with Non-Impact Aerobics

Many of us have discovered the wonders of Non-Impact Aerobics (NIA), a great workout experience that combines stretching with a "choreography" of fluid motions, along with proper breathing. The routines can be described as a blend of several activities including aerobics, ballet, muscle toning, and weight training.

NIA was developed by two aerobics instructors, Debbie and Carlos Rosas, who realized that high-impact aerobics can lead to serious injuries for those who jump into those challenging routines without good prior conditioning.

As for *body benefits*, NIA scores very high as a way to combat depression. It increases metabolism, respiration, and heart-rate—and also the production of those all-important neurotransmitting chemicals that give us the lift we need.

Good mental conditioning is also of benefit. NIA instructors encourage "mental conditioning" to help you achieve a positive frame of mind. Studies have shown that combining movement with positive meditations literally helps the brain to develop in healthy ways.

If you prefer, you can provide your own meditational experience using Scriptures or great thoughts from inspirational readings.

Do this:

- Check local community centers, gyms, and health clubs to sign up for NIA classes.

- Purchase a cassette of your choice. You'll find them available in many larger bookstores and through on-line book and tape sellers.

- As you engage the NIA routines, meditate on the truths that speak to you and allow your mind to be renewed and your spirit made lighter.

Recommended: *The Original Non-Impact Aerobics* (videocassette), Bod Squad, Inc., Vestron Video, Stamford, CT, 1987; and *The Ultimate Low-Impact Aerobic Workout* (videocassette), Kartes Video, Indianapolis, IN, 1987.

Strategy #8: Aerobics

Because we all tend to be less active in adulthood, few of us are physically ready to jump right into a high-impact aerobic workout. Far better to take time to work up to the more strenuous routines of high-impact aerobics.

On the other hand…if you're in that smaller percentage of the adult population that is reasonably fit, then aerobic exercise can give you the challenging workout and the therapeutic boost your body and brain chemistry needs. As with any other exercise program, one of the benefits of an aerobics workout is that it demands mental focus that gets you "out of your head" for a while and focused on a healthy pursuit.

Aerobics classes are easy to find by checking with community centers and health clubs. You also have a variety to choose from— from standard routines, to step aerobics, to "dancer-cise."

Do this:

- Visit a couple of aerobics classes to decide which type you want to try. If you tend to be self-conscious you might want to challenge that tendency by joining a class that uses a more graceful "dance" style. The sense of working through a mental barrier enhances good feelings about ourselves.

- *Be sure the instructor is attuned to your needs.* A good instructor will remember to—

  ❖ *begin* with a slower, warm-up pace

  ❖ *move through* a variety of paces and exercises

  ❖ *end* with a slower, cooldown pace

  ❖ *remind you* to let your heart-rate return to normal before sitting down

Three more words to the wise:

1. It's a great idea to see if the instructor or the facility has someone who is trained to know what to do in case of an injury or other medical emergency.

2. Get checked out by a physician before getting into high-impact aerobics. Besides the obvious, your physician will tell you what your resting heart-rate is and what your maximum target heart-rate should be during exercise.

3. If you're not going to be wise, and you ignore number two, at the very least check out your target heart-rate using the "*Target Heart-Rate Chart*" in this chapter. Monitor yourself throughout the workout.

Strategy #9: Weight Training

Weight training can offer more than the obvious benefits of a well-toned body. Several ways of approaching weight training can benefit us if we want to add this to our plan for overcoming depression.

You'll want to get checked out by a physician before getting into a weight-training routine. And you'll want to purchase good equipment or join a facility where experienced trainers are available to show you how to do the lifts correctly. (Yes, you *should* ask about their experience, and also how they're prepared to help you in case a medical need arises.) Good weight training requires know-how, or a lot of effort goes for little or nothing.

As an aid in lifting depression (no pun intended)…*do this:*

- *Imagine you are pushing back against depression.* Depression feels like a "weight" or like being stuck in a "closed-in" space. Sometimes we feel like we have "no room to move" in our decision-making. While you are lifting, imagine that you are pushing back the interior weight…pushing out the interior walls that confine you.

- *Affirm your hard work.* The sillier you think it is to tell yourself "good job," the more likely it is you need the affirmation. If you're tempted to think this is rinky-dink…get over it, come up with your own affirmations or use these as you pump iron:

  ⚕ "I *can* push back depression."

  ⚕ "I *am not* stuck or trapped. I *can* make decisions that, in time, will benefit me and change my life."

  ⚕ "I *can* become strong and healthy in body *and* in spirit."

Chart your progress. Reward yourself. Very often our depression is linked to a sense that we are doing thankless tasks. How long *has* it been since you got rewarded for a job well done—not for just any job, but one that directly, specifically improved you and the quality of your own life?

Too long? Never? You're overdue for some positive strokes. How about—

- telling yourself, "Great job"
- buying yourself new clothes that fit your new form
- accepting compliments when other people notice you're in better shape

WHY WE NEED TO REWARD OURSELVES

∾

A reward is simply a tangible way to mark an achievement. Achievements tell us "where we are" in various aspects of our life. Sometimes depression comes from the sense that we're wandering, aimless, going nowhere—or that we haven't accomplished much of importance.

Sure, it would be nice if others rewarded us for tasks well done but…it would also be nice if people didn't litter and paid their taxes on time. Whatever form our rewards take, we need to practice rewarding ourselves for these important reasons:

1. Most of us are starving for rewards that mark our achievements, whether in words or in the form of an actual prize.

2. Rewarding gives us good motivation to continue, especially when we're trying to form a new habit…or when the work is tough.

3. Rewarding is one of those habits we can use to benefit other people who are just as starved as we are for a kind word or a small prize to keep them from giving up.

If we're demanding of ourselves and stingy with personal praise and rewards… chances are good we are the same way with others.

Now is a great time to develop a generous, rewarding spirit…one that can lift others' spirits along with our own.

7

Natural Supplements

S *ome of the supplements discussed in this chapter are known to react with particular medications. Others will have an adverse effect on certain physical or health conditions—such as pregnancy, high blood pressure, and others. Some can also have adverse effects on certain types of depression, such as manic depression.*

As each supplement is discussed, some but *not all contraindications are mentioned. Consult your healthcare professional to create a treatment plan that is safe and right for you. You can find current information on herbs and suppliements on-line at www.consumerlab com.*

This chapter, which focuses on the use of vitamins, herbs, minerals, and other natural supplements in treating depression, has been placed near the back of this book for several important reasons. Consider them carefully.

A Moment, Please

The *main* reason for delaying the discussion of natural supplements in treating depression is that depression, as we've seen, has many possible sources. And when we become depressed, every aspect of our being can be drawn into its downward spiral.

For this reason, taking the whole-person approach to breaking free from depression is the *most* effective approach.

Second, strategies other than a regimen of natural supplements are known to work *as well* or *better*. Almost universally, health care professionals recommend—along with whatever else they suggest—a daily dose of physical movement (a.k.a. *exercise*).

So if you want to move out of depression…*move.*

Finally, we're a culture in search of quick fixes—preferably "oral fixes." We tend to think it would be great to pop a prescription drug or a supplement and experience miracle transformations. This is one reason why we're a culture full of unhappy, overweight, unhealthy substance-dependents.

Popping something in your mouth amounts to giving your well-being attention for just one moment in time... then walking away from greater needs that sent you down into depression in the first place. Nothing changes your life but *changing your life.*

Bottom line: Notice that the word is *supplement.* Whatever you take is meant to be used *in addition* to whatever else you are doing as you create a map and walk your way out of depression.

There is another reason to use supplements wisely.

Reasonable Concern

The mainstream medical community is still cautious about the use of nonprescription substances in the treatment of illnesses and disorders. Many healthcare professionals are especially cautious about (and some are against) the use of supplements in treating potentially serious conditions like depression.

The reasons for this are:

- *Medical schools have only recently begun to offer courses on complementary medical treatments and the use of natural supplements.* For this reason, not many medical professionals are knowledgeable in these areas.

- *Scientific research is ongoing as to the effectiveness of natural supplements.* Yes, this means their value is unproven to practitioners of traditional Western medicine. However impatient this makes some of us, caution and research are not bad things.

- *Natural supplements have sometimes been rushed to market...* and it's turned out that substances contained in them have harmful effects. Time and scientific research would likely have discovered this.

- *The traditional medical community is skeptical of "anecdotal evidence"...and not without good reason.* So much of what is trumpeted about the power of natural supplements comes from reports from everyday people—anecdotal evidence. This is not bad in itself. But it's possible that other factors that contributed to healing—maybe even the main factor—were actually left out as a person related a recovery story. (For instance, a man might report, "I was taking high doses of [X] at the time my depression lifted." But he forgets to say he also changed his diet, or got out of a terrible job, or began exercising regularly.)

- *The quality of natural supplements can be suspect.* Even if a natural supplement is effective, the production of supplements is not currently regulated. Quality can vary widely from batch to batch, even from pill to pill within the same bottle. This makes it hard to regulate the therapeutic value of any given dose.

Though attitudes in the medical community are changing about natural supplements, it's going to be some time before more is known conclusively, based on scientific studies, about their effectiveness. Meantime, these are not issues to be ignored, no matter how much we're in favor of using natural *versus* synthetic substances to treat our ills.

On the Plus Side

However there *is* a growing body of experiential and clinical (as well as anecdotal) evidence that natural supplements have greatly helped, and even cured, a wide range of illnesses and disorders. This evidence is in the form of countless personal testimonies. Those of us who have used natural supplements to alleviate depression and other health problems know how effective they can be.

Here are some of the benefits of using natural supplements:

1. *Natural supplements help the body heal itself.* Whereas synthetic drugs work by attacking and destroying, natural supplements work *with* the body's systems, building, strengthening, and supporting—taking the old "tonic" approach to creating physical well-being.

2. **Side effects are more easily noticed and countered before damage occurs.** The side effects of synthetic drugs can cause lasting damage, but natural supplements are generally gentler on the body. Though natural supplements can also have side-effects, most of them deliver milder doses of the effective ingredient and take longer to build up in the body.

3. **Putting time and energy into reading up on natural supplements can help us take a greater sense of responsibility for our own health and well-being.** Many of us need to take our health into our own hands after, perhaps, a lifetime of mostly ignoring our own needs or entrusting our wellness to someone else. Taking responsibility for ourselves is a definite psychological and spiritual benefit.

Clearly, some natural supplements have a reputation for providing relief from depression. The evidence shows they act to bring into balance physiological conditions that influence us emotionally.

If you decide to explore natural supplements, what follows is a list of those most commonly known to ease depression.

A Small Apothecary

The Vitamin Shelf

Certain vitamins are important to support the well-being of our body's nervous system. When they are depleted, the nervous system becomes stressed and cannot function properly. This has subliminal effects on our emotions, spirit…and eventually…on our thoughts.

We feel anxious…then tired and depleted. We're missing the sense that we are "equal to the day's challenges." We want to shrink back, draw in, avoid. Our state of vitamin deficiency triggers physiological depression.

Approaching from another angle…prolonged sadness or tension stresses our body, depleting our stores of physical energy. Since many vitamins are water-soluble, they don't remain in our system long. Under stress, the drain time can be very quick. Again, the end result is often depression.

Here are some descriptions of vitamins known to have mood boosting properties.

B-Complex Vitamins

The B vitamins, in general, are quickly depleted from our bodies when we experience tension associated with anxiety, grief, or fear. This family of vitamins is extremely important in helping many of the body's systems function well. Consider the following list, and you'll see why the depletion of B vitamins is likely to bring you down.

- **B1** *(Thiamin)* improves brain functioning, circulation, digestion, and overall energy

- **B2** *(Riboflavin)* improves production of hormones and red blood cells

- **B3** *(Niacin)* improves the release of energy from all foods, controls cholesterol, cleans toxins from the body

- **B5** *(Pantothenic Acid)* assists in the production of hormones, red blood cells, Vitamin D

- **B6** *(Pyroxodine)* assists in the production of enzymes, hormones, proteins, and lowers homocysteine levels in your blood (elevated homocysteine levels being associated with confused thinking—even stroke and Alzheimer's disease)

- **B7** *(Biotin)* improves the release of energy from carbohydrates

- **B9** *(Folic Acid)* lowers homocysteine levels, helps prevent birth defects

- **B12** *(Cobalamin)* is crucial for red blood cell and energy production

More specifically, B6, B9, and B12 help in the production of the neurotransmitter serotonin, which promotes a sense of balance and well-being—improving our ability to bounce back from life's greater and smaller "downs." Maintaining the proper amount of B1 promotes a stable calmness.

In cases of severe and prolonged depression—except for manic depression—a physician may give intramuscular injections of B vitamins in higher therapeutic doses.

Additional Notes:

➔ B vitamins are most effective when taken with meals.

➔ The absorption of B vitamins can be inhibited by taking certain medications—including common antacids, penicillin, and oral contraceptives, so you should take these medications 12 hours apart from your doses of B vitamins.

Other B Vitamins

- *Choline,* part of the B vitamin family, is also important in boosting brain function, and can be helpful in clearing the mental confusion that accompanies depression.

  Warning: Choline should not be used by those suffering with manic depression, as it may worsen your condition.

- *Inositol* is also in the family of B vitamins. It helps maintain higher levels of serotonin. Higher doses of inositol have also been shown to relieve panic attacks, but this therapy should not be tried without the supervision of a healthcare professional. Inositol should be taken in combination with B-complex vitamins.

Vitamin C

This vitamin is most commonly associated with the improvement of immune function. It also helps the adrenal gland produce antistress hormones, which promote an all-over sense of well-being.

Vitamin C with bioflavanoids is recommended. If you take C in higher doses than the standards recommended by the Food and Drug Administration, be sure to drink higher amounts of water—16 ounces at the time of the dosage—or kidney stones may result.

THE AMINO-ACID SHELF

Amino acids are used in the building of healthy cells and muscle tissues. For this and other reasons, they're important for promoting healthy biochemical processes throughout the body. A deficiency in amino-acid intake stresses the body, contributing to "body-based depression" and to depressive moods.

A Caution: Remember that amino acids = protein. *Too much protein can be toxic to the kidneys and liver.* High-protein diets and the overuse of amino-acid supplements (for dieting, muscle-building, and toning, and even for "health" purposes) can cause this toxicity.

If you are using amino acid supplements for a long period of time, you should be under the guidance of a physician and have periodic blood work done to check kidney and liver function.

A WORD ABOUT "MULTI'S"

∿

"Multi" vitamins and vitamin/mineral combos…usually do not provide adequate doses of the vitamins and minerals needed. That's because vitamins and minerals tend to wash through and out of the body fairly quickly. So your "once in the morning" dose may not be around many hours later when your body most needs the help. *And* you may be paying for some vitamins and minerals you don't even need.

Taking a multivitamin once a day is to taking supplements what overloading on breakfast and then starving the rest of the day is to food energy.

On the other hand, taking a multivitamin is better than nothing…especially if you're busy and can't keep up with multiple doses throughout the day. Truthfully though, scheduling two times a day for supplementation is not *that* difficult—say, at breakfast and dinner (or bedtime).

If you want the most benefit from your supplements:

1. Research what you specifically need.

2. Take *only* what you specifically need.

3. Know which supplements need to be taken with food.

4. Drink a minimum of 8 ounces of water…preferably 16 ounces, especially if you are taking several supplements at once.

5. Keep track of all supplements you are currently taking. This information may be needed in a medical emergency, as some natural supplements and drugs react badly to each other.

The following amino acids are helpful in mood-boosting efforts. You should "test" their effectiveness for you by trying each, individually, for 10 to 14 days.

- *Acetyl-l-carnitine.* ALC helps energy production within brain cells. In short, it can help create the "mental boost" so missing in our depressive thinking and moods. ALC also assists in the

transmission of nerve impulses in the brain, and it helps protect brain cells against blood-borne toxins.

- *L-creatine.* Possibly you've heard the hoopla about the use of
creatine for bodybuilding. This is because creatine stimulates
brain functioning by promoting the use of the neurotransmitter
chemicals. In short, it promotes clarity of thought and the effi-
cient use of nutrients at the cellular level—adding up to sharper
mental focus and a sense of being energized.

    For this reason, using creatine can enhance your workout. You
    may want to use it along with one or more of the physical strate-
    gies for depression relief suggested in chapter six.

- *L-phenylalanine* offers mood-boosting benefits because it stimulates brain function and the production of serotonin. It also
has a "peaceful" effect because it stimulates the release of endorphins, the body's own natural opiates.

    Phenylalinine can have noticeably stimulating effects almost
    immediately. When taken in recommended doses, its greatest
    benefits are realized over time.

    *Never exceed the manufacturer's recommended doses of pheny-
    lalinine* because this substance is easy to abuse. It's often mis-
    used at "raves" and at "smart bars" to give abusers the rush
    they're looking for without the inebriating effects.

    Warning: *Do not use Phenylalinine if you suffer from anxiety or
    panic attacks or both, as it can make the condition worse.*

- *Phosphatydil serine.* PS is a phospholipid, which means it's a
"fatty" substance used in the building of cell membranes
throughout the body. The highest concentrations of PS are
found in brain cells. There, it boosts the healthy activity of those
all-important neurotransmitting chemicals. Also, it helps nutrients enter and wastes exit the brain cells.

- *S-adenosylmethionine.* SAM-e is one of three natural substances
most often recommended for lifting depression by practitioners
of natural medicine. It's an amino acid that's responsible for cell
growth, DNA repair, immune response, and much more.
Without it our bodies begin to break down at the cellular level.

    Such factors as stress, depression, a meat-based and highly
    processed diet, and arthritis and other diseases that chronically

GOOD "SCENTS"

～

"Aromatherapy" has emerged in recent years as a way to treat depression. Essential oils are sold in kiosks and shops everywhere.

Skeptics argue that the scents themselves do nothing... and that the benefits only come from the fact that we naturally breathe deeper (that is, we breathe properly) as we take in those wonderful scents. They say it's the breathing *itself* that induces greater blood oxygenation, better metabolism...and a sense of mood elevation...so why "waste" the money?

But if breathing properly is "all there is" to aromatherapy— that's actually a very good reason to try it! Any scents that cause us to breathe deeply make good sense.

Practitioners, including trained herbalists, insist however that we should not take aromatherapy lightly. The scents of certain essential oils have been shown to benefit specific conditions, like depression. Other scents, though, are reputed to trigger unwanted physiological responses.

To lift depression...you may wish to try:

basil	vanilla	lavender	bergamot	cedarwood
lime	melissa	orange	chamomile	peppermint
geranium	jasmine	ylang ylang	sandalwood	rosewood

To use essential oils:

✤ Mix 3 to 5 drops of essential oil into a tub of warm water.

✤ Mix 10 to 20 drops of essential oil with 1 to 2 pints of water in a spray bottle and mist the room.

Pregnant women *should not* use the following essential oils: basil, bergamot, cypress, geranium, hyssop, marjoram, melissa, peppermint, sage, thyme, or wintergreen. Check with an aromatherapy expert or a knowledgeable healthcare professional before using any essential oils during pregnancy.

tax the immune system are responsible for the fact that many of our bodies cannot naturally produce the SAM-e we require. SAM-e benefits our overall physical wellness and helps create mood buoyancy. In fact, some its users claim it works faster and is just as effective as tricyclic antidepressants.

- *L-tyrosine.* Like phenylalanine, this amino acid can have stimulating effects almost immediately. It works by boosting the production of the brain's mood-enhancing neurotransmitting chemicals.

    Warning: Do not use tyrosine if you are on an anti-depressant of the MAO-inhibitor type.

THE HOMEOPATHY SHELF

Homeopathy is definitely one of those approaches to depression relief best undertaken with the help of an experienced practitioner. It's basic idea is that "like cures like." The substances that are given are said to stimulate the body to resist the disease or condition it's suffering from. Which substances are used will depend on important variables in your condition. Also, the dosages are minute…as are the adjustments that need to be made to keep them working as your condition changes.

The substances a homeopathic practitioner is likely to recommend are these:

- *Aurum Metallicum* is often used when a person reports feelings of worthlessness and despair.

- *Causticum* is often recommended when someone is generally gloomy and negative…or "caustic." It's also sometimes recommended by practitioners when feelings of foreboding or anxiety are frequent, or when tears are easily triggered.

- *Cocculus* is sometimes recommended for depression associated with sleep deprivation. (Of course, you could just work on getting more sleep….)

- *Gelsemium* has a range of uses. It's said to be helpful for mild, general depression—and also for depression caused by severe shock, such as that caused by sudden and terrible news, and the emotionally "frozen" state accompanying such shocks. It's also used for the depression that can come in the aftermath of a draining physical illness.

- *Ignatia Amara* is also often used in cases of depression caused by emotional trauma—especially grief caused by the loss of a someone well-loved. It's said to work effectively for those who carry a sense of "lostness."

- *Lachesis* is often used for those whose depression comes from suppressed emotions—such as anger and jealousy. Reputedly it helps the user release those emotions, which then helps resolve the interior conflict causing the depression.

- *Sepia* is often used when depressive symptoms include emotional exhaustion, indifference, or weariness with living.

To locate a homeopath in your area, contact The American Institute of Homeopathy at (703) 246-9501.

THE HORMONE SHELF

Hormones regulate many important body functions. For this reason, you should proceed slowly when using a hormone supplement. As with other supplements, begin with a low dose and allow time for the hormone to show its effects on your system before increasing to a higher dose.

These hormones are often recommended for depression:

- *DHA* (docosahexaenoic acid) is one of the omega-3 essential fatty acids. (See chapter 5 for dietary information on EFAs.) In the body, it's the main substance needed to build the brain's gray matter and the retina of the eye.

    Our main dietary food source of DHA is the oil of certain cold-water fish. In fact, evidence for its use in relieving depression comes mainly from the fact that societies that consume high quantities of fish suffer far less depression—about a *tenth*—than societies in which fish is not a main protein staple.

    Because we eat less fish than any other population on earth, North Americans have the lowest levels of DHA on earth. Certainly other factors come into play, but we also have by far the highest rate of depression.

Warning: *If you want to get your DHA by taking fish oils, you need to know that these also contain EPA, which acts as a blood thinner. For this reason, food products or supplements containing EPA are* not *recommended for pregnant women, infants, the elderly, diabetics, or those taking prescription blood thinners.*

- *DHEA* (dehydroepiandrosterone) is a hormone that has been used in the self-treatment of depression in recent years. It's a precursor to estrogen and testosterone…and so you can imagine the claims that are made about its ability to boost the sex drive.

  Research has shown that DHEA has significant mood-and energy-enhancing effects, and that it can promote deep and restful sleep without the morning "hangover" of sleep medications.

- *5-HTP* (5-hydroxytryptophan) is another of the three natural substances most recommended for the treatment of depression. 5-HTP helps in the production of tryptophan, which in turn contributes to increased levels of (you guessed it) serotonin in the brain. It has replaced tryptophan in the marketplace (when that supplement was removed from shelves), and so far it has proven to be safe and effective in depression relief.

EPHEDRA WARNING

～

Healthcare experts are warning against the use of ephedra…an herbal stimulant that is sold in products that claim to relieve conditions including depression. Often it is sold in "quick stop" stores to give drivers a "buzz" to keep them awake on the highway. Sometimes it's sold under the name *ma huang.*

Ephedra can be dangerous. It hits the heart and respiratory system with a powerful jolt, which is of course where the "rush" comes from. That in itself is dangerous. Along with that, its effects on the nervous system seriously deplete the body…and then it wears off, triggering a big let-down.

When it comes to using ephedra…just don't. Safer natural stimulants are on the market.

THE HERB SHELF

Though "milder" than pharmaceutical drugs, herbs can also have side effects, and certain herbs can interact badly with medications. You should check with your pharmacist, physician, or herbalist before mixing herbs and pharmaceuticals.

When starting an herbal treatment, it's best to start with a low dose. Give the herb time to work before increasing the dose. When buying herbs you should look for those that are organically grown. If you can work with a trained herbalist, so much the better.

And unless you are a highly trained herbalist, it's best not to harvest herbs in the wild. Too many safe herbs can be confused with poisonous plants.

Here are the herbs most often recommended for their mood lifting benefits:

- *Black Currant Oil, Evening Primrose Oil.* These two wonderful plant oils are high in essential fatty acids (EFAs) needed by every cell in the body. Long-term grief and stress can deplete the body of EFAs. This can create a deep, lasting fatigue, depression, even arthritis-like symptoms as connective tissues in the joints fail to repair themselves.

    For this reason, people experiencing such conditions as depression, chronic fatigue, and rheumatoid arthritis can benefit greatly by using these natural plant oils. Besides assisting the body in healing itself, both of them act as natural pain relievers. Neither is known to have any side effects.

- *Gingko Biloba.* Gingko is well known for its ability to boost brain functioning and help promote mental clarity. (My elderly father's joke about gingko is that he used to take "this wonderful herb that helped his memory a lot" before…but he stopped taking it and now can't remember its name.)

    Gingko is often recommended to help clear up the frustrating "woollyheadedness" that can accompany depression.

- *Guarana.* This natural stimulant is a mood lifter, and a much better choice than ephedra. Its "lift" can last for many hours, so you may not want to use it later in the day, when it's likely to prevent you from falling asleep at your normal bedtime. Before-noon use is probably best.

Herbalists often use guarana to treat people suffering from mild depression. Or they may suggest one of the two following herbs instead....

- *Kola nut.* Like guarana, kola nut is a stimulant whose effects are slightly more intense and long-lasting than the caffeine in coffee. Unlike guarana, kola nut users sometimes experience a rush of energy and a mild tingling sensation.

  Higher doses of kola nut can have the reverse effect, pushing you through an "up phase" back down into a slowdown phase. As with any substance, start slowly, with a low dose, and work up.

  Whereas guarana can be found in capsules by itself, kola nut is most often found in "energizing formulas" in combination with other natural substances. Be careful to read what those other substances are, and leave the formula on the shelf if it contains *ephedra* (a.k.a. *ma huang*). Occasionally you can find kola nut by itself in powdered form or concentrated drops.

- *Maté* works as a stimulant, much like guarana and kola nut. It usually comes in leaf form, sold as a bagged or loose tea, though it can also be found in extract form.

  Large doses of maté can overstimulate you, causing insomnia. It also has diuretic properties, and so its overuse can cause dehydration.

- *St. John's Wort (Hypericum perforatum,* sometimes just *Hypericum)* is the third of the three natural substances most commonly recommended for depression, and is widely reputed to lift the symptoms of mild to moderate depression. An extract from the plant is blended with the dried, crushed herb itself and is sold in capsule form.

  Use of St. John's Wort will increase sensitivity to sun exposure, so take extra precautions to limit your exposure when taking this substance.

"OTHER" SUBSTANCES

Throughout our society certain substances have become widely used to escape depression. This is because they temporarily alter our perception of reality.

I am referring to *alcohol* and *narcotics.*

When we're down, stressed, or just want to "get out of our heads for a while," using alcohol and drugs seems like a good idea. It is, in fact, a very bad idea.

Alcohol depletes the body of vitamins, minerals, and healthy nutrients. Narcotics (prescription and illegal) greatly affect brain chemistry, as does alcohol…and not to our benefit.

If you are depressed, stop using alcohol immediately. Likewise, if you are misusing prescription drugs or using an illegal substance… stop. *If you need help to stop, seek it today.*

A final word: Prescription medications can be a great blessing when they bring relief from suffering…including depression. They are sometimes the best solution for immediate and lasting relief from depression…but they are only to be used under the direction of a physician.

8

Maybe Your Life Needs to Change

*B*y now you should have been able to identify the mood-lifting strategies that will fit your situation and preferences. Because they're natural remedies, they'll take time to work…but they *will* help you to break free from depression.

Because we're all unique, each of our paths to personal wellness will be slightly different. You should feel free to try out the various strategies until you find the ones that work best for you. You should also be aware that strategies that work today may not be as effective in time. You may want to refer to this book again and pick up new ideas as necessary.

Life is About Change

On a greater scale, we can find even more help by refocusing our attention, not on strategies per se, but on the bigger picture into which depression usually fits.

Often our depression exists in a larger context. That context is our life—or rather our view of life, our feelings about life, and the values that tell us how we want our life to be.

Sometimes depression is a sign that a great *life transition* has begun. We've been living in one set of circumstances, finding our sense of well-being in seeing things one way, relating to people in one way, wanting things to be one way…and then…

Then one day our inner compass seems to be confused. The old maps and the charted courses we were following don't work anymore. We may begin to feel as if we're not even on the right continent. But where do we go from here? Our natural instinct is to try to hold on to the past, those familiar ways of thinking and living. But they're old and outlived. Or gone. We no longer "fit" there.

I am speaking in figurative language to describe something of what it's like to find ourselves faced with making a transition. Transitions are absolutely necessary to personal growth. That's because life is all about change—those that happen *to* us…and those that go on *inside* us.

Unfortunately, few of us are told to expect this in adult life. We thought we were going to hit 21, or 30, or 40 (some "mile marker") by which time we'd "have it all together." No one told us that life is all about transitions, much less how to face and go through them.

And so we give in to a natural instinct, which is to cling to the old and familiar. We grasp at ways of thinking, ways of living, that used to let us feel in control, or at least comfortable. But new outer and inner realities present themselves—and what we need is to change, stretch, and grow. We need to crawl out of the cocoon we spun as a caterpillar, when something inside us was okay with settling down right where we were…and we need to emerge to become what we must be *now*.

If we continue to cling to our old ways of thinking and doing and being, the new life we now need cannot unfold and take wing. Often it's the fear of this newly emerging life that is, in fact, the great and true reason for our depression. We're depressed at a core level of our being because we're not allowing the new person we need to *be* to be born.

If we're unable…or refuse…to complete the necessary transition—through the letting go of an old self so we can emerge as a new self—we're likely to stay stuck in depression for a long, long while. Maybe the rest of our lives. Hopefully, the consequences of making this choice are too dark for you even to consider.

How can we recognize the need to make a major life transition?

Consider some common transitions you may have already experienced by this point in your life.

Grief after a move. When we live in the same place for a long time…especially, say, an area in which we grew up…it's common to experience depression after moving away. Before the move, we may have even told ourselves we were tired of the area and ready for a change.

But then comes the transition to the chosen new area. We feel excited at first, and go exploring. We begin to locate not only "replacement" grocery stores and doctors...but replacement "parents, brothers, and sisters," and new buddies. But in time a slow, creeping numbness can take hold. We sleep more. Fixing up the new house slows, then ceases. Six months...a year...two years after the move...we're sunk in depression.

College Freshman "dis-orientation." We are *so* ready to leave high school—those same old faces and cliques, the confining rules. So ready to take charge of our choices, our schedule. Really, really ready to explore life "out there."

Then comes the day when we kiss Mom and Dad goodbye (quickly, before they get embarrassingly teary), and the period of new discovery begins. Here are new ways of thinking, adults who treat us like adults, interesting new people who cannot be "slotted" into one of the old high school categories (jocks, cheerleaders, computer geeks, "Magic, the Gathering" players, drama queens, goths, thugs, "ghetto pretenders"...). The world is full and opening up.

Then on your way across campus one day, you feel a knot in your throat. For "no reason" there are tears. What are you doing here? How did you mess up your checkbook and max-out that credit card already? This is not like you. Maybe you'll make a call later...talk to Grandpa, Dad, Mom...or even the little sister you couldn't wait to get away from. Maybe surprise them with an unscheduled visit home. (*Geez*. What *is* wrong with you?)

And maybe...halfway through your first semester, when all those little blips of homesickness ought to be over...the cold sweats begin. You wake up in a real panic. Heart racing. You want to quit school tomorrow...but you're torn because that would also feel like quitting and going home with your tail between your legs. For days you agonize, talking yourself *into* staying...and *out* of staying...as indecision keeps you twisting inside, and depressed.

Newlyweds' and new parents' remorse. Maybe you've spent a bit too much money on a new car...and as you drive that sleek machine home you feel as much regret as pride. This is called "buyer's remorse," and it's similar to the kind of remorse newly-weds and new parents may experience.

Newlywed remorse can hit as early as the honeymoon...or in the first three years, judging by the huge percentage of divorces that occur by the third year. We had one thing in mind...but we got another. We hoped certain feelings would end. We hoped isolation would be engulfed in intimacy, and longing for touch would vanish in the presence of tenderness and attentiveness incarnate.

New-parent remorse is harder to face...because parents shouldn't feel panic or grief or feel "trapped" when they're holding their sweet little angel from heaven, should they? Guilt and shame make new-parent remorse hard to admit.

Unfortunately, many of us "disconnect" from the relationships we're in. Some walk out literally. Others stay...but never build true intimacy or experience mutual support for growth and fulfillment. We live out a long, gray disappointment in the context of depressive—as opposed to supportive, spirit-lifting—relationships.

"Excuse me, have you seen my life? It seems to be missing." Some at-home mothers get this definite but unnameable sense after awhile. So do people who have any sense of their own skills, potentials, and even a flicker of a dream about what they want to become...and then wind up settling somewhere short of their dream. Yes, we made the choice we're living with now. Yes, some accommodations are necessary in life.

But why are we feeling more restless and depressed with each passing year?

Perhaps we forgot that the choices we made were supposed to be only for a time. The job we took was supposed to be a stepping-stone to the position we really wanted. The choice to be at home with the kids was the best choice—for that time and place. The accommodations we made to build another aspect of our lives were for *then*...but *now*....

Now other creative energies have been growing...and finding little or no outlet. Now we see someone who's doing exactly what we wish we were doing. And all that thwarted energy stirs.

If we feel "stuck" where we are because of "circumstances," or lack of training, or insecurity about setting out...we'll feel like we're living parallel to our own life. There it is...over there...and someone else is living it in our place! Then comes grief…and depression. This is often closely related to…

The mid-life…or late-life…meltdown. We imagined that by 35, 40…certainly by age 50 or 65…we'd be—settled? Sure of ourselves? Happy and at peace? Accomplished in our work?

People in midlife have no corner on this market. Gradually, or suddenly, many adults of any age wake up one not-so-fine day after youth is long gone…to disillusionment, discouragement, depression. Or maybe to a "quiet panic"—the desperate sense that we need to scramble as fast as possible away from the life we have if we're ever going to experience the life we crave.

We may dye our hair, get buff, run off to somewhere else with some*one* else…but as the saying goes, "There *we* are." Whether we stay or run, we carry depression that sometimes borders on despair…that we have missed some "secret" or some important turning point "back there" that would have made us fulfilled.

The shaking or collapse of beliefs. Somewhere in our past we experienced a *conversion*—political, spiritual, or what have you. We accepted a whole ideology that, at the time, filled our deep need to make sense and meaning of the world. Maybe it was a radical conversion and we have spent years recruiting people casually or very actively to our position.

And now we're faced with a change just as radical. Maybe our beliefs eroded slowly, one tenet at a time. Or maybe we've seen that the beliefs we hold in our head have not had the power to make us the kind of persons we want to be—and the now-apparent gap between our "doctrine" and our life is a chasm whose walls are collapsing, leaving us sinking into a sense of lostness and depression. We feel profoundly disoriented.

If we were so sure those were the right answers…and they may not be right or complete after all…what do we believe now? How can we face all those people who think of us as a staunch [whatever we were]?

Symptoms

Each of the above scenarios represents a transition. Some are minor. Some are major. We've lived in one context—a physical, emotional, intellectual, or spiritual "setting"—and some great shift is occurring. Down beneath the unseen "bedrock" on which our soul once stood firm, vast tectonic upheavals are slowly or suddenly altering us at the core.

All at once it dawns on us: This life we're living is changing. Maybe it needs to change. Maybe we're waking up to the fact that it's never going to be what we pictured. In any case, it's also dawning on us that all our efforts to shape and tame life, to fix it just the way we want it—all our work, our relational strategies, our deeply held beliefs—all these efforts are amounting to little or nothing.

Something very big and important is happening. Or it *will* happen, if we learn how to get through the deep insecurity and fear that comes with interior upheavals…and learn how to step into the new context the upheaval is presenting us.

But before we examine that, it will be helpful to understand the first stages of what's going on here:

Actual reality is catching up with our "view" of reality. Yes, Virginia, there is an actual reality out there, and it can be greatly at odds with the picture we've always had of the way we want life to be. Reality usually does run counter to the "script" most of us draft for our lives. It can run counter to our ideology (political, spiritual, economic, social) about "the rules" for living.

In our view, reality should work something like this:

"If I believe the right things…

…act the right way…

…follow the right steps to success…

…am a generally good person…

…*life will generally work out the way I want and need it to.*"

By "working out" we mean something like "I will have few disappointments, no tragic losses, no injustices."

But forces in the real world are always at work to move us out of the above "charmed and childlike" thinking wherein we need to see ourselves as safe, secure, and protected. Instead, the real world periodically has a way of jumping out and shouting, *"Surprise!"*

When we don't want to let go of our old thinking, when we fear and resist the "big world" out there and what it might do to us…we shut down. This is when we spiral into depression. We're so heavily invested in seeing things work out "our way" that we lose flexibility. We're like a guy standing rigid on a surfboard, frozen, unable to subtly shift and rebalance himself—which is what makes it possible to ride the rise and fall of a wave. Or the changes of life.

We brace against the new. Moving to a new area, or going to college…getting married…having a baby…these steps in life give us *some* of what we wanted.

But the new place or relationship was no miracle cure. The new has not given so much *to us* as we'd hoped. Maybe the old feeling of not fully belonging is still there. And the new is also asking for something *from us.* We're handed more work and responsibilities. If we give in to what it demands, maybe something in us will be forgotten…given up and lost for good.

Down in our essential being—our soul—we brace ourselves. If the new is not what we'd hoped…if it asks more than we think we can give…shouldn't we keep it at a distance?

We believe—mistakenly—that hindsight is always 20-20. We *believe* we can see everything more clearly in hindsight. But it's questionable *how* clearly we really see our past. Counselors say we tend to idealize the past—either making it much worse than it was, or much better. When we're pressed about the real details, the "golden eras" of our lives very often turn out not to be so golden after all. It's just that we mourn the loss of certain places, people, feelings, experiences. And we cling to the mistaken idea that if we could "go back" all would be well. We may also tell ourselves that the fact that the river of life and time that's ever-moving is a rip-off.

However, we may see some things about ourselves…and others… more clearly from a distance. It seems we *do* tend to be more honest about our motives and desires when we look back at them. We seem to make more honest admissions from a "safer," that is, "more mature" position. Yes, we were fools to do the hurtful…and to resist the good. Perhaps we can make these admissions because it feels "big" and "mature" to be honest about the person we "used to be."

We also tend to be more open to others who tried their best to do us good in our past. We're more generous toward the parent who pushed us hard back then when we didn't want to be pushed. Living in paradisal Hawaii, we now miss the friend we took for granted when we trucked it fast out of frozen Tundraville. We can easily slide into depression when we're stuck in mourning about our own past blindness.

We resist work...especially relationship work. Any time we make a move to deepen a relationship, there is *real work* to be done. We're challenged to strengthen our connections to another. We must learn how to give what they need...and how to ask for what we need...and how to "negotiate" the differences between what's hoped for and what's really possible.

And while all these hopes and expectations are fueling our dreams...something inside us is resisting the work it takes to haul those dreams out of thin air and bring them into real life. That resistance is the force of fantasy thinking:

Wasn't this new spouse or partner supposed to understand us? If they were our "true soul mate"...if they cared about us more... wouldn't they automatically know what we need? Wouldn't they be more sensitive and notice what we like? Why do we have to open our mouths and ask...or even argue...for what we need?

And as for this new baby...aren't we supposed to feel nothing but proud and happy around this sweet new angel? Does this child really have to demand so much of us?

*And...why do we feel so uncomfortably self-centered feeling the way we do? How do we adjust to this sense that we can't be "just for ourselves" anymore?—that we're not only individuals but "corporate" selves too...*part of a family, not its center?

As we pass certain "mile markers" in life, the inner shifts seem greater...until they trigger "earthquakes."

We seem to carry inside ourselves certain "markers" by which we judge our own success or fulfillment as human beings. For some of us, it has to do with a position we hoped to achieve, or a certain level of power and authority. For others it has to do with level of income...or freedom to be creative...or the arrangement of a comfortable or interesting lifestyle.

Along with these markers, we also carry our own sense of timing about when this level should be reached. Generally, we pick an age—be it 29, 46, 50, or 83—by which we want our life to "come together." As that number approaches, we feel restless and unhappy.

If we hit *that* age and have not reached *those* mile markers...we slide into depression. All that we *have* done, we minimize. We say of our accomplishments, "It wasn't important"—when what we mean is, "It didn't make *me* big or important enough in my own eyes."

We could take apart any of these life scenarios and examine it in finer detail. We could look at factors that formed our expectations. An unloving father. A too-ambitious mother. Other deprivations of childhood. Important as these things may be *to a point*, the past will not tell us what we need to know about living well in the present and future.

For that, we need to know that the world, and our own lives, are in a constant state of change. We ourselves are constantly faced with the need to make *transitions*. Much of our depression comes from not understanding what it takes to go through a transition.

But once we see our lives in this context, we can learn how to live as people in transition. It's not that we'll stop experiencing loss or disappointment, but we are likely to suffer less from them. By taking the ups and downs of transition in stride, we're apt to experience more stability, peace…and find that we're not so likely to be thrown into depression.

Life in Transition

As we observed at the outset, life seems to be all about transitions. As we reach adulthood life seems to become more like a constantly shifting landscape…parts of it eroding…new challenges thrusting themselves up out of nowhere…tremors shaking us… maybe even some devastating earthquakes.

The truth is, few of us seem to know how to do transitions well. We like security, often even when our lives have become so dead and dull as to be unbearable. "Sameness," even when it's killing our soul, seems preferable to the unknowns of risk and change.

The *other* truth is, if we don't learn how to ride out life's changes—the wanted, the unwanted, and the necessary—we are dooming ourselves to depression in its various forms.

Here are some of the temptations we face when we're approaching a major transition:

- *We take the powerless victim stance*—blaming other people, or even God, for our depression and dissatisfaction.

- We stay stuck in "kicking myself for this" mode—as if self-punishment will do any good.

- We destroy the life, job, or career we have—when the truth is that gradual, planned, well-thought-out change usually works out better than "desperate" moves.

- We foolishly abandon the people already in our lives… thinking a "change of personnel" will somehow get us to our dreams.

- We "medicate" our depression…by drinking…or finding some victim to unload our endless complaints upon…or with illegal substance abuse…or overeating…or….

GOING THROUGH TRANSITIONS SUCCESSFULLY

A quick look at unhealthy ways of handling our need for change shows at least one thing clearly: The dreams and drives—the original spark of our creation—*will not go away.* The energy *will* go somewhere…either for ill purposes or healthy ones.

What we need to know is how to use the energy of our dreams and drives in healthy ways. This is essential if we're going to make the transitions of adulthood, move ourselves out of depression, and do so in ways that are not destructive to ourselves and others.

What are some healthy ways to direct our energies wisely?

1. Identify More Fully with Our Present Place

We often assume that in order to move on to a life that's whole, full, and rich, we *need* to abandon the person we've been and the life we've lived. This may be true for some of us, but it isn't a universal need. There is no law written on the back wall of the universe that says, "Thou shalt leave what thou art doing and become more fulfilled somewhere else…with someone else."

Sometimes the transitions we must make are subtler. We are deeply rooted where we are because we *value* where we are…and always will.

If this is the case, we need to direct our energy toward *greater identification with the role we're in and the people we're living with.*

We will need to:

- *Redirect the energy of our dreams* of being somewhere else, doing something else, with someone else. To do so, we realize how much our dreaming "scatters," weakens, and depletes us...until we are making little or no valuable contribution anywhere. We gently turn aside those tantalizing temptations to move on...and our energy gathers into a happier focus on where we are and what we're doing.

- *Take stock of the life we have.* Treasures have lain buried in art museums, libraries, and attics. Someone recently found a rare document, worth millions, by closely examining a framed print they bought for a few bucks at a flea market. What have you been overlooking that's of great value in the life you're living? Is it true you're "getting nothing out of" your work, your relationships— or have you just taken things for granted?

  Can you honestly say there is nothing new to learn about your relationships or your work? Is there no new contribution you can make where you are? Are your skills *really* unnecessary...or are there new challenges you can use them for?

- *Get "distance" from your life and work.* We need to work hard. And we need breaks. Sometimes we really are made for a marathon run of exactly what we're doing right now. But mostly what we desperately need is to adjust our pace and intensity. A simple shift in our calendar...a change in work hours...and we feel more rested and free. And often during our breaks, creative new ideas come.

- *Find someone to train.* Often we find a new purpose and energy in our life, not by leaving what we're doing, but by reaching back to train someone who is coming after us. Subtly, we shift into the role of mentor...and find ourselves making a fulfilling new contribution.

All these ways of focusing in on the life we now have and the work we're now doing have healthful affects. By identifying more closely with where we are—putting body, mind, and soul into it anew—we subtly but definitely change our identity. We engage the power we have to change the place we're in. And with these changes, in us *and* our work, comes a quiet but nonetheless miraculous lift in our mood.

Life is moving in us, and through us, once again…

2. Face the Transition...and Walk Out the Changes...to Someplace New

When life brings us that "lost-on-the-globe" kind of depression, our other big choice is to wisely, carefully walk out the changes we need to make. Sometimes this, the work of changing our lives, is the only and best solution to our depression.

To take ourselves through a big life transition, we need to:

- *Recognize and honor the fact that, for us, change has become essential...not negotiable.* Maybe the change was thrust upon us—as in the case of losing someone we loved, or a job we liked. Maybe the thought of creating a new future during such a mandatory transition just makes us feel tired and lethargic.

  What we need to do first is to honor the past. We do this by considering long and hard what we *valued* about it. We cannot always hold onto the situation or relationship we have been in— but we can carry away with us the things we esteemed there.

- *Take our treasures with us as we go.* What we valued, what we believed in…this is what we take with us from one place, position, job, or relationship to another. We know that as long as these interior valuables go with us, to be used again in creating our new situation, *we*—that is, our essential self—will not be lost in the shuffle.

  Certain spiritual teachings emphasize "letting go," but they don't make one vital distinction. That is, we must learn to *let go* of outer circumstances (and sadly, sometimes people) whose place in our life has become unhealthy or destructive or out-lived—while we *hold on* to our core values. Even though we must all learn when to let go of the outer, none of us can ever let go of the inner core without causing great harm to ourselves.

- *Let go...and trust.* Once we've determined which circumstances have outlasted their usefulness and which inner values we must take with us…it's time to let go and move on.

What we have to let go of, we can do with grace and dignity and without regret. The new situation we're moving toward may be clear…or it may not be. *Trust is essential.*

Trust is the belief that when we move, God comes to our aid. We don't expect everything to go smoothly: We may make a few missteps. We are, after all, blazing a new trail for ourselves, going where we've never gone before. We may need to let go of something besides our old situation—namely, our need to have everything smooth and to never make mistakes. Like explorers, we keep on moving ahead, one step at a time, trusting that the way *will* become clearer and *will* open for us.

- *Accept a period of chaos… insecurity…and no sure direction or answer.* We put such a premium in our culture on being definite. On focus, and on knowing exactly where we're going. There is a downside to this, because only as we embrace times of questioning, *un*knowing, and exploring…*without a definite goal*…do we ever discover the truly new.

  As we go through some of life's most important transitions we will feel pushed, by ourselves or others, to say *exactly* what we're going to do or be. ("So, Farnsworth, you've left your job and you're 'not sure' what you're going to do, eh? Does that mean you're going to be a *beach bum*?")

  To go through transition, we need to accept the unsettled feelings that unsurety and nondirection give us. Leaving one definite place for a place not yet "set" *feels* as chaotic as it *is*. It's time to stop telling ourselves that a little chaos and uncertainty (that is, being out of control) will hurt us. The uncertainty of transition is necessary and will *not* hurt us.

- *Make no fast moves, no quick decisions…just to quiet our fears, or those of other people.* If we accept that some of life *is* chaotic, we are less likely to let the discomfort of this uncertain period force us to make moves we'll regret later. Especially moves that cause us to settle for something far less than the new situation we're looking for. Though we feel out of control in times of transition, the events surrounding us are not out of God's control.

  One of the things that's going on inside us is that we're learning how to live above the pressure that other people put on us. If we don't easily fit into a recognized role (banker, computer consultant...husband, wife) others feel uncomfortable. Let them deal with their own discomfort. Our task is to follow through to become what we must be.

- *Use the time to plan...and to watch for the new opportunity.* Once we've made a definite step away from the old, what we want and need from the future can become a bit clearer. But what about the present? The present we use for practical matters.

  → *We plan.* What steps must we take to get to the new?

  → *We assess.* How much of our dream is—here it comes—realistic? Will we have to settle for, if not the dream itself, something *close* to our dream?

  → *We rest.* Rest? Exactly. Rest is a very practical thing. More so for some of us who don't know how to rest. And it will help us gather energy to jump in whole-heartedly, not burned out, when the new comes along.

In fact, some people going through transitions find themselves needing more sleep. Transitional times can be emotionally, physically, mentally, and spiritually depleting. We carry a constant underlying anxious tension ("What am I going to do?") or grief ("What will I do without _____?"). Because of this, we're open to physical, emotional, and spiritual ailments.

We should not mistake our need for rest during this time as laziness. It can be absolutely necessary to counterbalance the emotional and spiritual energy we're using to "maintain"...let alone search for the new. Proper rest is necessary to keep us from slipping into a body-based depression.

- *We renew our commitment to God.* To believe we were made with a purpose we must fulfill is to believe in the God who made us with purpose. And so we renew our commitment to working in cooperation with God, so we can find the life we were created to embody, and do the tasks we were created to carry out.

- *Watch for the old "markers"...in a new setting.* Remember the old "markers"—those *values* we held before—which told us whether or not we were on track? We will carry most of our deeply held values with us throughout life. *We need them now.*

We usually do not lose or change our values. But what *does* change during the transition is the way we live in relation to them. For example:

The woman who knows and values the power of money is likely to still value the power of money even after leaving her career as an investment broker. But she is likely to transition from living for the purpose of making money to, say, living to teach others how to use it wisely or for charitable and philanthropic purposes.

The man who loved systems and the sights and sounds of a well-designed business organization is likely to bring his value of design and symmetry to the handmade furniture or musical instruments he leaves the high-tech world to spend his days creating.

As we emerge from a period of transition, we're likely to find in our new situation that what we have always valued is coming back to us in a new form.

The person who has lost a loved one—through estrangement or death—is likely to emerge from grief and depression as they become a surrogate father, mother, brother or sister, grandparent. And also emerge wiser and more compassionate for their loss.

- *Welcome the new…with all your strength.* Stepping into a new role, a new relationship…this can be as hard as any of the other aspects of a transition. This is because it can be the final, ultimate act of letting go. It is to let something or someone real step into the place of the old, which is now only a memory.

  Success…reaching new goals…leaving an old identity behind…it's odd how we humans relate to our new beginnings. Whether the transition was something we chose or not, we can feel guilty, disloyal, undeserving, selfish. We can experience a wave of nostalgia, even grief.

  These feelings may be the final rise and dip of the waves that picked us up and urged us to move on from the life we were living, the people we once were. If we ride them out, they will pass…leaving us standing on a new shore.

GENERATIVITY

We set out to look at our depression in the greater context of our whole life. Many of us who have come through long and serious bouts of depression have discovered that though various strategies helped, *nothing helped us break free from depression as much as learning to find and live out a deep sense of purpose.* For various reasons, this deep sense of who we were and what we were to become lay buried under the debris of other, lesser purposes we once spent all our time and energy living for.

Then came depression…and the soul's dark night…and a transition to a new life.

What we discovered is that there is an original spark of drive and creativity that was always there in us. It was a dream that had to be hauled out of the images swirling in our heads and made real. It was work we had to do.

Personally, I take this original spark to be the light that God ignites in each one of us.[4] It was not meant to be hidden under a bushel basket.[5] It is easily misdirected…sometimes used for limited, even self-centered, purposes.

A half-century ago, psychologist Erik Erikson coined the word *generativity.* It's my belief that the drives and dreams placed in us by God are the fires that *generate* and drive our need to create, build, nurture, correct, discover…our need to make this world a better place…and our need to keep on growing in physical, mental, emotional, and spiritual wholeness long into our old age—for as long as we will follow the God-given life-spark that is in us and find the lifework we were sent here to do.

It is my personal hope that you will honor the life that is within you. That life is a gift. That gift is you, yourself, as you become the whole person you are meant to be. Your purpose is a gift, too: Your struggle to find it and live it will take you on from depression until you are doing the work of your life—a masterwork only you can do.

In closing…I wish you courage, and a lifetime of well-being.

NOTES

1. The Epistle to the Philippians 4:7.
2. For a complete guide to balanced eating, read *Mastering the Zone,* Dr. Barry Sears (New York: HarperCollins, 1996).
3. Ecclesiastes 7:16,17.
4. Psalm 139:13.
5. The Gospel of Matthew 5:14,15, RSV.

THE NEW NATURE INSTITUTE

The New Nature Institute was founded in 1999 for the purpose of exploring the connection between personal health and wellness and spirituality, with the Hebrew-Christian tradition as its spiritual foundation.

Drawing upon this tradition, the Institute supports the belief that humankind is created in the image of God. Each of us is body, mind, and spirit, so intricately connected that each aspect of our being affects the others. If one aspect suffers, our whole being suffers; if all aspects are being supported, we will enjoy a greater sense of well-being.

For this reason, the Institute engages in ongoing research in order to provide up-to-date information that supports a whole-person approach to wellness. Most especially, research is focused on the natural approaches to wellness that support health and vitality in the body, the mind, and the spirit.

Healthy Body, Healthy Soul is a series of books intended to complement treatment plans provided by healthcare professionals. They are not meant to be used in place of professional consultations and/or treatment plans.

Along with creating written materials, The New Nature Institute also presents seminars, workshops, and retreats on a range of topics relating to spirituality and wellness. These can be tailored for corporate, spiritual community, or general community settings.

For information contact:

The New Nature Institute
Attn: David Hazard
P.O. Box 568
Round Hill, Virginia 20142
(540) 338-7032
Exangelos@aol.com